CONTENTS

Introduction

Surrogacy and IVF is the eleventh volume in the series: **Issues For The Nineties**. The aim of this series is to offer up-to-date information about important issues in our world.

Surrogacy and IVF looks at the ethical and medical issues relating to surrogacy and in-vitro fertilisation.

The information comes from a wide variety of sources and includes:
Government reports and statistics
Newspaper reports and features
Magazine articles and surveys
Literature from lobby groups
and charitable organisations.

It is hoped that, as you read about the many aspects of the issues explored in this book, you will critically evaluate the information presented. It is important that you decide whether you are being presented with facts or opinions. Does the writer give a biased or an unbiased report? If an opinion is being expressed, do you agree with the writer?

Surrogacy and IVF offers a useful starting-point for those who need convenient access to information about the many issues involved. However, it is only a starting-point. At the back of the book is a list of organisations which you may want to contact for further information.

*****

Considering surrogacy?

Your questions answered

What is surrogacy?

A surrogacy arrangement is one in which one woman (the surrogate mother) agrees to bear a child for another woman or a couple (the intended parents) and surrender it at birth. This provides an opportunity for those women who are unable to carry a child themselves to overcome their childlessness.

Distinction can be made between 'partial' and 'full' surrogacy. In partial surrogacy (also known as traditional or straight surrogacy) the surrogate mother provides the egg. The sperm from the intended father will be placed into the surrogate mother's vagina, either by the surrogate mother herself (self-insemination) or by a health professional and fertilisation will then take place in the usual way.

With full surrogacy (also known as host or IVF surrogacy), the surrogate mother has no genetic link with the child but gestates embryos which are usually created from the eggs and sperm of the intended parents. Assisted reproduction techniques will be used, such as in-vitro fertilisation (IVF or the 'test-tube baby' technique). This involves the collection of eggs from the intended mother and sperm from the intended father and placing them together in a laboratory. One or more embryos will then be placed into the surrogate mother's uterus for gestation. A maximum of three embryos can be replaced but more often it is limited to one or two to reduce the chance of a multiple pregnancy. If the intended mother is unable to produce eggs herself, an embryo can be created from the sperm of the intended father and eggs from an anonymous donor, again using the IVF technique. Similarly, if the intended father is infertile, an anonymous donor's sperm can be used to fertilise eggs from the intended mother using IVF. An information leaflet about the technique of in-vitro fertilisation is available from the Human Fertilisation and Embryology Authority (Paxton House, 30 Artillery Lane, London E1 7LS).

Who might use surrogacy?

Some women are unable to carry a child to term. A variety of causes account for this, including failure of the embryo to implant, repeated miscarriage, hysterectomy or a pelvic disorder. Some women experience problems such as dangerously high blood pressure, a heart condition or liver disease, so that pregnancy would entail a serious health risk for them.

Some people may come to terms with their childlessness. Others may find adoption or fostering an acceptable alternative, although this option is limited by the number of babies and children offered for adoption. For others surrogacy may be seen as a possible solution. Because surrogacy involves another person taking on the risks of pregnancy, it is only acceptable as a last resort, where it is impossible or very dangerous for the intended mother to carry a child herself.

Sometimes people speculate about women taking part in surrogacy arrangements, although capable of bearing children themselves, because they wish to avoid the physical, social, psychological or financial drawbacks of bearing a child themselves. There is no evidence to suggest that this happens in Britain and it would not be seen as an acceptable use of a surrogacy arrangement.

What is the legal position?

Surrogacy is not prohibited by the law. However, it is illegal for an individual or agency to act on a commercial (i.e. profit-making) basis to organise or facilitate a surrogacy arrangement for another person. Agencies or individuals may perform this function on a non-commercial basis and individual surrogate mothers may be paid expenses by the intended parents. All advertising that a person is willing to be a surrogate mother or that someone is looking for a surrogate mother is prohibited.

The law states that any clinic providing treatment involving the donation of eggs or sperm, or the creation of embryos outside the body, must be licensed by the regulatory body, the Human Fertilisation and Embryology Authority (HFEA). Full surrogacy, which involves the creation of embryos outside the body, must therefore be performed in a licensed clinic. Where the insemination with the intended father's sperm, in partial surrogacy, is performed by a health professional (thus using donated sperm), the premises on which the procedure takes place must also be licensed by the HFEA.

Are surrogacy arrangements legally enforceable?

No. Surrogacy arrangements are unenforceable in law. Therefore, irrespective of whether a contract has been signed, and whether any money has changed hands, either party could change its mind at any time. For this reason, it is particularly important that all parties have considered very carefully the implications of their decision to take part in a surrogacy arrangement. If any of the parties have any doubts

about their commitment to the arrangement, they should say so before a pregnancy is established and the arrangement should not proceed.

What is the legal status of the child?

In law, the legal mother is always the carrying mother (i.e. the surrogate mother in a surrogacy arrangement). The identity of the legal father is rather more complicated. If the surrogate mother has a partner he will be the legal father of the child, unless he can show that he did not consent to the treatment. If the surrogate mother does not have a partner and the treatment did not take place in a licensed clinic (i.e. it was self-insemination), the intended father will be the legal father. If treatment was undertaken in a licensed clinic and the surrogate mother has no partner, the child will be legally fatherless.

This has a number of implications. In order for the intended parents to become the legal parents of the child, they must either apply to adopt the child or apply for a parental order (see below). This is true even if they are the genetic parents of the child (i.e. their sperm and eggs were used). If the intended parents change their minds about taking the child, for example, if their circumstances have changed or if the child is born physically or mentally disabled and they feel unable to cope, the surrogate mother and her partner, if she has one, will be legally responsible for the child.

What is a parental order and who can apply for one?

A parental order, which is obtainable by application to the courts, makes the intended parents the child's legal parents. This has the same effect as adoption, but allows a quicker route in cases of surrogacy.

In order to apply for a parental order, the following criteria must be met:

- the child must be genetically related to one or both of the intended parents;
- the intended parents must be married to each other and must both be aged 18 or over;
- the legal mother and father (i.e. the surrogate mother and her partner, if she has one) must consent to the making of the order (this consent cannot be given until six weeks after the birth of the child);
- no money other than reasonable expenses has been paid for the surrogacy arrangement unless the payment has been authorised by a court;
- the child must be living with the intended parents and one or both of the intended parents must be living in the UK;
- an application must be made within six months of the birth of the child.

A child born to a surrogate mother will be registered as her child and that of the legal father (see above). Where a parental order has been granted a separate entry will be made in a Parental Orders Register. However, it is not possible to abolish the original birth registration and at the age of 18, the child will be able to obtain a certified copy of the original record which will include the name of the surrogate mother. Prior to being given access to this information the person will be advised of the availability of counselling.

Will the surrogate mother have contact with the intended parents and the child?

This will depend upon the individual circumstances and the wishes of the parties concerned. It is important that this is discussed from the beginning so that problems do not develop at a later stage when the different expectations of the parties become apparent. Some surrogate mothers find it helpful to have the support of the intended parents throughout the pregnancy and equally the intended parents often want to share the experience and be involved with the pregnancy such as attending hospital for scans and possibly being present at, or immediately after, the birth. Others prefer to have limited contact.

Once the child is born the level of contact will again depend upon the wishes of the individuals concerned. In some cases, contact stops, by mutual agreement, as soon as the child is handed to the intended parents, except for the communication required for transferring the legal parentage of the child. In other cases the intended parents will send photographs of the child to the surrogate mother and in some cases the child will know the surrogate mother and her other family. What is important is that the surrogate mother and intended parents agree on a level of contact which they feel is appropriate for them.

Who else might be affected by the surrogacy arrangement?

Although the main parties to the arrangement are the intended parents and the surrogate mother, there are wider implications, and before proceeding, the effect on other family members needs to be considered. For example, the surrogate mother's partner, her parents and any existing children will also be affected. The partner may feel a sense of bereavement at losing the child his partner has carried for the last nine months and unless very sensitively handled existing children may be disturbed by the loss of a sibling and fear that they also may be 'given away'. For the intended parents' family there may also be anxiety and uncertainty.

The child's grandparents may find it difficult to accept the method of the child's conception and may treat the child differently from other grandchildren. Other children may find it difficult to accept their new brother or sister and may resent the attention given to the child by their parents. With careful handling all of these difficulties can be minimised but consideration should be given to these issues before deciding to proceed.

What are the implications for the child?

One question which all intended parents have to deal with is whether to tell the child of his or her origins. Research shows that most people who have children conceived by surrogacy decide to explain the circumstances of their conception and birth to the child. If parents decide not to tell, they face a number of difficulties. Surrogacy is difficult to conceal from others, and if other people know bout the arrangement, there is the risk that the child may find out from them. The experience of learning in this way, and the discovery of deception by his or her parents, may be very distressing for a child. Another factor to be considered is that at the age of eighteen the child will have the legal right to discover the identity of his or her surrogate mother.

The number of children born as a result of surrogacy arrangements is small and there is a very limited amount of research available into the effects on the child. However, it has been suggested that such children may feel a certain amount of anxiety about being 'different' from their friends and may sometimes feel pressure to live up to the expectations of their parents who went to such great lengths to have them. However, these concerns do not appear to reflect the reality for children from other 'different' families, such as those resulting from infertility treatment or adoption. More positively it has been suggested that children conceived via surrogacy arrangements may in fact be proud of their parents' courage and grateful to their parents, and the surrogate mother, for their existence.

What happens now?

Surrogacy might be the only opportunity for some people to have children but it is not something which anyone should enter into lightly. Before deciding to enter into a surrogacy arrangement, either as a surrogate mother or an intended parent, it is important that the information contained in this booklet has been carefully considered and understood. It is a good idea to obtain as much information as possible, take time to reflect on it and, if possible, discuss it with partners, family or friends. Anyone with doubts about their commitment to surrogacy should not proceed any further.

• The above is an extract from *Considering Surrogacy?*, issued jointly by the British Medical Association and the Human Fertilisation & Embryology Authority.

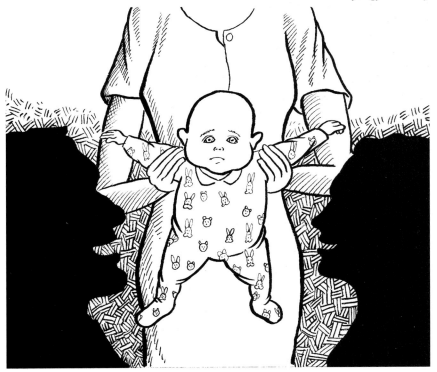

Guide to surrogacy

Information from C.O.T.S. (Childlessness Overcome Through Surrogacy)

C.O.T.S. launched, appropriately, on Mothering Sunday in March 1988 with only 70 members behind us for support and encouragement together with the united ambition to establish public awareness for a vital need and available solution for childless couples everywhere. We are a voluntary organisation whose aims are to help, advise and support both infertile couples and surrogates. Triangle is a subsidiary organisation of C.O.T.S. and actually puts couples and surrogates in touch. Both organisations work together. C.O.T.S. is run mainly by the chairperson, Kim Cotton, who has been a surrogate mother herself twice, doing both straight and host surrogacy and the secretary, Gena Dodd, who has a surrogate son through straight surrogacy. Between them they felt they were able to advise others, as Kim knew what it felt like to relinquish children, and Gena how it felt to receive one.

One in six couples will experience some problem with infertility. Most overcome their infertility with hospital treatment, but for some no amount of medical treatment can help. These are couples where the wife was born without a womb, women who have had a hysterectomy for whatever reason, women who have had multiple miscarriages etc. For these couples and others there is not much hope. Adoption is virtually nil in this country and this is where surrogacy can and does help.

Surrogacy is where a woman carries a child for an infertile couple, be it straight or host surrogacy.

Straight surrogacy: is where the surrogate artificially inseminates herself with the intended father's sperm. Therefore the baby she parts with is genetically her own.

Host surrogacy: is ideal where the wife of the couple has no womb, or is unable to carry a child for whatever reason, but her ovaries are working normally. Using the IVF technique the couple's genetic embryos can be transferred into a surrogate. So basically the surrogate is only acting as an incubator to the genetic child of the couple.

> *One in six couples will experience some problem with infertility. Most overcome their infertility with hospital treatment, but for some no amount of medical treatment can help*

The couple can, on a private basis, make an agreement where the surrogate is paid for her expenses and for looking after the child whilst in her womb. This is not illegal but no agreement is binding by law and at any time either one can back out, so basically it is done on trust.

The positive aspects of surrogacy are that, if the couple are lucky enough to find a surrogate and everything goes according to plan, they have a child that is either the husband's, or as in host surrogacy, genetically theirs. We always recommend everyone has medical tests i.e.: HIV, hepatitis (B), cystic fibrosis etc. (and rubella for the surrogate). It is compulsory that all couples and surrogates see a counsellor/mediator for an 'information giving session' before they embark on an arrangement.

On the negative side though, if the surrogate decides to keep the child she has a perfect right to do so. The law states that the birth mother is the legal mother. The couple have also to take into consideration that the child might be stillborn or handicapped either physically or mentally or both, but these risks are there even if they were to have a child of their own.

Ever since our launch the reputation of C.O.T.S. has continued to grow world-wide to accommodate over 600 members and an astonishing 277 surrogate and potential surrogate mothers, willing to make the ultimate gift for childless couples from all around Great Britain and beyond. The result has been the births of 200 surrogate children in the last nine years from the inspired concept of C.O.T.S. These include 19 sets of twins and 1 set of triplets. This record is up to February 1997.

We now work in close contact with IVF hospitals involved with host surrogacy and are extremely fortunate to have lists of independent social workers, psychologists, counsellors/mediators and solicitors specialising in the subject of surrogacy.

C.O.T.S. and Triangle accept any infertile couple under the age of 45. They must, if the woman has a womb, have been to an infertility clinic and gone through all medical channels available.

Surrogacy is not an easy road to take. One has to think long and hard about it before embarking on the lengthy and hazardous journey. It is a last option, not a first. We only suggest surrogacy when all else has failed.

Our organisation is in regular contact with ISSUE, CHILD, PPIAS, PROGRESS, HFEA, BMA and the Department of Health.

C.O.T.S. has aroused much interest in many quarters and has been asked to supply information to the following professional and medical organisations: PAGIGS (Professional Advisory Group for Infertility and Genetic Service), the BMA (British Medical Association), HFEA (Human Fertilisation and Embryology Authority) and numerous other Government

Surrogacy really should be the last resort. The hazards are innumerable, the rewards unbelievable

bodies. We have also had enquiries from government and hospital bodies from various parts of the world. Subsequently we send out many *Comprehensive Guide to Surrogacy* booklets each year to various hospitals, doctors, students, teachers, libraries and, of course, the media.

In response to requests by numerous hospitals to give talks to doctors and their students, our executive committee and lay members have given several lectures to Women's Groups, BMA, SERONO, CHILD and The British Fertility Society. C.O.T.S. has chaired two seminars in the last two years.

Over the years we have collated an abundance of information in the form of books, videos and leaflets,

for reference for both C.O.T.S. members and the general public.

As the organisation has grown we now have a wider panel of people who have experienced surrogacy for themselves in one way or another. They have made themselves available to help others who are planning to follow in their footsteps. We have helplines that couples and surrogates can phone, we also have chatliners who phone up couples and surrogates while they are going through an arrangement, so that no one is left feeling isolated.

All potential couples and surrogates are seen by an independent counsellor/mediator for an 'information giving session' before they are placed on our active list.

By the time infertile couples consider surrogacy they will have exhausted all possible infertility treatment available to them, or alternatively have medical confirmation that conceiving and bearing a child of their own may be a life-threatening experience. Surrogacy really should be the last resort. The hazards are innumerable, the rewards unbelievable. It is something they both have to desire equally.

C.O.T.S. Executive
Committee '97
© C.O.T.S. 1997

Personal experience

Information from C.O.T.S (Childlessness Overcome Through Surrogacy)

Cheryl

I first read about surrogacy and C.O.T.S. on the problem page of the Christmas *TV Times*. At the time I was divorced and living on my own. I already had four children, my family was complete, although I was perfectly capable of having more children.

I received all the literature and although it answered some of the questions, I still hadn't decided. It took me three months to decide I wanted to help a childless couple. During the next eighteen months I met two couples. Both backed out,

one for medical reasons, the other for domestic reasons. Finally I met Tina and Mike. On the day they visited us, I ran round tidying the house and the kids ran round untidying it again! My stomach was doing somersaults. When they arrived we said our hellos and sat down with a drink, I told Tina all about myself and what had happened over the last 18 months. She told me all about her and Mike and how they'd been trying for a child for over ten years. They gave me a photo album with all their family in, and I showed them photographs of my own family, we

were all getting along really well.

When they left I couldn't help thinking how different this first meeting had been compared to the previous two couples. Tina and Mike would really have gone to the ends of the earth for a child.

Soon after we had our first try. Sadly, it didn't work, Tina said 'never mind it was only the first try' but to me it was yet another month of failing. Trying to get pregnant for Tina and Mike was so stressful for me, the two weeks of waiting, wondering and hoping that maybe this time. I'd already been through eighteen months of this, I can only imagine how women felt trying for years and years.

We tried again and as the day drew closer for my period to come, all the tension started again for me. I got out of bed the day my period was due and rushed to the bathroom, no period! I must have gone to my bathroom fifty times that morning just to check. On one such trip there it was, I'd come on. I sat there crying, how could we have missed again? I felt terrible, maybe I wasn't meant to be a surrogate mother. I phoned Tina to tell her the bad news.

By tea time I'd noticed that my period wasn't as heavy as usual, it had more or less stopped and by the time I went to bed there was nothing there at all. The next morning when I woke there was still nothing. I bought a pregnancy kit just to make sure.

The test proved positive, I was pregnant! I couldn't believe it, why had I started bleeding yesterday if I was pregnant? The doctor explained that sometimes it's common for women to have spotting just before they find out they're pregnant.

I tried to get in touch with Tina, I was so frustrated that I couldn't. Eventually I contacted her, I asked her if she was sitting down and she said 'yes', so I just said 'I'm pregnant', she couldn't believe it. At about six thirty Mike phoned to say well done, he was chuffed to bits. After all this time it had finally happened, it really was like a weight being lifted off me. I was helping a childless couple.

Tina and Mike were over the following weekend to celebrate. I went into town to buy some tiny white boots and a book called *A Thousand Mothers' Questions Answered.* That afternoon a big bouquet of flowers arrived for me saying 'Well done, we've done it.' It was really nice of them.

I decided now was the time to tell my children exactly what was going on. They already knew that Tina and Mike didn't have any children because Tina's tummy was 'broken', and for a couple of weeks I'd been showing them the photos of Tina and Mike's house and telling them how quiet it must be with no children. Then I got back on to the

---

I decided now was the time to tell my children exactly what was going on

subject of Tina's tummy being broken, so she couldn't have a baby in her tummy the way I'd had them in my tummy. I explained how she'd love to, but because of her poorly tummy she couldn't and that made Tina and Mike very sad. After a few minutes one of my children said, 'But you had us in your tummy', I said, 'Yes' and she said, 'Well you could have Tina's baby in your tummy.' I said what a good idea, and because they suggested it, it was brilliant. To them it was just normal, so I had to explain that not every mummy would do this.

When Tina and Mike arrived I gave her the presents and card. The tears rolled down her face as she looked at them. One of my children told Tina that mummy was going to have a baby in her tummy for her and Mike so they could be happy. I felt very proud because all their happiness was because of something worthwhile that I was doing.

We'd already talked about the birth, Tina was giving up work around Christmas and we suggested that near the time she would stay at my house. I really enjoyed our special days together but thinking ahead after the baby was born all the special times together would end because they would be parents with a child of their own.

In my mind I knew I would give the baby up, but at that time I couldn't honestly say I knew how I

was going to feel about it. With all the hormones and body changes after having a baby nobody can tell you that you're going to feel this or you're going to feel that, everybody is different.

Around sixteen weeks it was time for my first scan. Tina came with me, she was very excited, we could see everything. Its little legs looked like it was riding a bike. Tina held my hand and just gazed at the screen, for the very first time she could see her perfect baby, her whole face just lit up.

At the end of January I was called for another scan and Tina came with me again. She'd finished work and spent most of the days looking at baby clothes and airing the sheets for the cot and pram. We didn't have long to go as my second scan put me one week forward.

In the middle of February Tina came to stay at my house until the baby was born, and Mike joined us at weekends.

One Saturday morning I felt sure something was going to happen, but I felt fine and we all went to Blackpool as planned. On the way home my bump went rock-hard for a minute it was a little uncomfortable then it stopped. I sat there hoping it would do it again and this would be it. About ten minutes later it did happen again and for the next half an hour it carried on. I didn't say anything because it could have just gone away as fast as it had started. I kept looking at Mike's clock to time the tightening, at this stage I never had any pain but I knew something was imminent.

I had a bath when we got home, I then decided that I had better tell them what was happening. I really hoped it wasn't a false alarm now that I'd told Tina and Mike.

The contractions started to come at different times, sometimes every twenty minutes then every ten then back to every twenty. By ten o'clock I decided to go to bed. I finally got to sleep around half past twelve but by three o'clock I was awake again. I remember lying there watching the clock and hoping I would get another contraction. After twenty minutes or so I decided to go downstairs to make a cup of coffee.

I went to the loo and had just got into the bedroom when my waters broke. I woke Tina, the way she reacted you'd think the fire alarm had gone off, she jumped out of bed and shook Mike telling him to get up.

We all sat drinking coffee and talking, just after six I reached down to the floor to pick something up, and as I did, I had an enormous pain. I felt the baby drop right down. The pains started getting stronger and stronger and Tina held my hand as Mike drove us to the hospital.

At twenty past seven the midwife came, they moved me to delivery. At this stage I can honestly say I didn't like the midwife and I hated her even more when she unplugged the mask from the gas and air bottle and wasn't taking it with us. All I wanted was the gas and air but Tina was by my side and that was all that mattered. The next thing I heard was someone asking me if I wanted to push, I answered 'yes'.

At seven thirty on the dot it was all over. I asked Tina what it was and she said 'a baby', her face was full of delight and she couldn't keep her eyes off the baby. I think I'd just put her through the most worrying hour of her life. I asked her again what it was and she said 'a boy'. I asked the midwife if he was all right and she said 'he's perfect'. I just held Tina for what seemed like ages, then I told her to tell Mike he had a son.

Tina couldn't keep her eyes off him, I looked at him and said 'hello' then passed him to the arms of his mum. Tina stood there, tears rolling down her face, there was nothing needed to be said. The midwife left the room and Tina just couldn't stop saying 'thank you' and 'I'll never put anyone through that again.' She sat down still cradling her son, talking to him all the time.

Mike walked in with smiles all over his face; just an hour before he'd dropped us off and now he could hold his new-born son, Scott.

I didn't feel sad as I watched them both gazing at Scott, I felt so proud of myself for ending their ten year battle for a child. I never once thought about keeping him, I could only think of the happiness I'd caused and that Tina and Mike were finally a family.

At twelve fifteen we were discharged. We registered Scott, as we came out of the registrar's office Mike gave me a cuddle and said 'thank you for everything', I told him that I had no regrets at all, I'm just pleased it was me that helped them because they were so caring and supportive all the way through the pregnancy. When we got back to the car Tina was talking away to Scott, she told me it felt like one chapter of her life had closed and another one had opened.

We drove slowly back to my house not really knowing what to say to each other. All I could think of was if I was Tina or Mike I'd now be wondering if I was going to get out of the car and really let them take him. At this stage all I wanted to do was get out of the car, not because I was upset, just so they knew this was all real and actually happening, and after all these years they finally had a son.

When we parked outside my house Tina said, 'I don't know what to say now.' I told her not to say anything. I gave them both a hug, said goodbye to Scott and told them to get going. I got out of the car and waved goodbye and went into the house.

I've never cried over what I've done. I feel that I've done something really worthwhile in my life. I know not everyone can understand how anyone can do such a thing and they think it's unnatural but all I can say is if it wasn't for women like me then a lot more couples would be going through life just wishing and hoping that one day they too could have a family.

• Since then Cheryl has given birth a second time for Mike and Tina, another son, Brett, born in 95. She is now currently pregnant for another couple.

The above is an extract from *C.O.T.S. Guide to Surrogacy*, published by C.O.T.S. See page 39 for address details.

© C.O.T.S.
1997

Womb service

1985: Kim Cotton becomes Britain's first surrogate mother. She is paid £6,500 by an American couple, leading to a public outcry. She gives birth after one of her own eggs is inseminated artificially. Ms Cotton is also paid £15,000 by a newspaper for her story.

1985: The Surrogacy Act makes it illegal to profit from surrogate agreements, though 'reasonable expenses' may be paid. In June 1991 Ms Cotton gives birth to twins on behalf of a friend but is not paid.

1987: Pat Anthony, 48, from South Africa, becomes the world's first surrogate grandmother after she was implanted with eggs from her daughter, Karen. She bore triplets.

1990: Human Fertilisation and Embryology Act requires infertility centres to be licensed and introduces fast-track procedures for legal adoption of surrogate babies.

1995: An unnamed couple are granted full parental rights for their surrogate child. The landmark ruling means the couple bypass complex and costly adoption procedures.

1996: British Medical Association changes policy and advises doctors to discuss surrogacy with couples where appropriate. It defines 'reasonable expenses' as £7,000 to £10,000.

1996: First NHS-funded surrogate birth is planned at King's College Hospital, London.

© *The Guardian*
December, 1996

Responding to surrogacy

Information from the Christian Medical Fellowship (CMF)

Who is my mother? . . . Who is my father? . . . Fairly simple questions – any two-year-old could tell you the answers. Indeed, for most people reading this, the questions will not pose any problem whatsoever. However, there are some for whom these questions will pose a difficulty – those who are adopted or illegitimate and, a smaller group, those who are born as a result of surrogacy.

What is surrogacy? What is all the fuss about? Surely, if it helps someone to have a baby then it must be all right? I would like to look at these questions and examine 'what the fuss . . . is about'.

Although there is no established or documented evidence, it appears that informal surrogacy (where conception occurs by natural intercourse) takes place not infrequently in Britain.[1,2]

How does surrogacy work?

Surrogacy means simply 'taking the place of someone else'. A surrogate mother 'carries a foetus and bears a child on behalf of another person, having agreed to surrender that child to this person at birth or shortly thereafter.'[1]

The procedure involves a couple (the commissioning couple) who wish to have a child and a woman (the surrogate) who offers to carry that child through pregnancy for them. The couple are known as the commissioning couple and the woman is known as the surrogate. The oocyte (egg) and sperm which unite to form the embryo may come from a number of sources. The egg may come from the surrogate, from the female partner of the commissioning couple or from an anonymous donor source. The sperm may come from the male partner of the commissioning couple or from an anonymous donor source. Fertilisation of the egg may be by sexual intercourse, artificial insemination or in-vitro fertilisation (IVF).

The availability of surrogacy is very limited in Britain. In the small number of units where it is available, the general practice is to carry out IVF on the commissioning couple by collecting the woman's eggs after hormone stimulation and mixing with the man's sperm. After those involved have been screened for HIV and hepatitis B infections. The resulting embryos are transferred to the uterus of the surrogate mother, usually after freeze storage for a number of months so that HIV and hepatitis B status of those involved can be confirmed as negative.

Possible indications for surrogacy

Surrogacy may be an option considered when an individual couple are unable to conceive or the female partner is unable to carry a pregnancy for whatever reason. The possible indications for its use are summarised in Table 1. They are divided into those based on medical grounds and those based on question-able (or even spurious) grounds.

The legal situation relating to surrogacy

The Warnock Report (1984), the Surrogacy Act (1985) and, most recently, the Human Fertilisation and Embryology Act (1990) taking affect from August 1st, 1991 – contribute to the legal background to surrogacy in this country. Up to the time of the Warnock Report was published, there was no regulation of surrogacy practices in the country. The members of that body strongly recommended that 'the activities of agencies and individuals to arrange for surrogacy services be [regarded] criminal, professionals knowingly assisting in this be [regarded] criminal and all such contracts to be [regarded] illegal'.[3]

The Surrogacy Act (1985) made it an offence to arrange, agree about or take part in a commercial arrangement for surrogacy.[4] It is not, however, an offence to take part in these arrangements when there is no element of gain or commercial interest. Surrogacy is carried out on a commercial basis (according to this Act) if payment is received by a third party for it, or if it is carried out with a view to payment being received. Payment for the necessary expenses of the (prospective) surrogate mother is allowed. It is also an offence to advertise that one is either looking for or willing to be a surrogate mother through any medium (TV, radio, newspapers), apart from word of mouth.

The Human Fertilisation and Embryology Act (HFEA), passed by Parliament in 1990 and entering into law in August 1991, amended the Surrogacy Act so that surrogacy arrangements cannot be enforced by law. The commissioning couple may become legal parents of a child born as a result of a surrogacy arrangement, although the child is legally the child of the surrogate mother until then.[5] The current legal status is summarised in Table 2.

The areas of legal concern relate to the wide constraints put on the practice of surrogacy by the law, as already pointed out, and the inability of either party to enforce the arrangement. In essence, this means firstly that it is very difficult to find a surrogate or to offer oneself as a surrogate and, secondly, that if the surrogate mother decides she wants to keep the child, she cannot be prevented from doing so; likewise, if the commissioning couple decide they do not want to take the child, they cannot be forced to do so.

Biblical background

There is very little mention of the practice in Scripture and we must look to two chapters in Genesis (16 & 30) to learn what we can. In chapter 16, God had made a covenant with Abram promising him many descendants and his doubt in that promise made him take alternative action. At Sarai's suggestion, Abram took his servant-girl Hagar to his bed and she conceived. The result of this was distress and emotional turmoil for all concerned. Hagar despised Sarai, after which Hagar was ill-treated by Sarai. Hagar gave birth to Ishmael, who lived in hostility towards his brothers. Abram's action was not out of step with the cultural mores of the time; his sin was not to wait for God to fulfil his covenant.

Jacob also had children by the servant-girls of his two wives (Genesis 30). This came about because of jealousy between his wives and, while Jacob does not appear to be directly contravening God's direct promises here, the result of his action was continued dissension and dissatisfaction in his family for quite some time.

When the references in Scripture allude to the practice of 'surrogacy', the inference seems to be that it involved either a failure to wait for God to fulfil a very specific promise or sinful attitudes to a marriage relationship. Is it too much to infer from this that the practice is viewed by God as, at best, a poor second best or, at worst, being outside his will for us because of its effects?

Areas of ethical concern – a Christian perspective

The ethical dilemmas here relate to asking an individual woman to carry the pregnancy of a couple who for some reason are unable to do so. Within the context of a heterosexual (married) relationship, the conception and carrying to birth of a child as well as the responsibility and the small (but not insignificant) risk involved is accepted as being an integral part of the relationship. The attitude of God towards the marriage relationship is that it is both for companionship[6] and for procreation[7] but he does not clarify what his view

is (from the passages in Genesis 16 & 30) on the practice of surrogacy.

However, to bring in a third party who is not a part of this relationship means asking that individual (woman) to take on these risks and responsibilities on a voluntary basis without the benefits of companionship and support. It is this major step, I think, that makes surrogacy so contentious.

Areas of ethical concern – secular perspectives

Difficulties arise when counselling both the prospective surrogate mother and the commissioning couple to ensure they understand what is involved. The areas which need to be covered include the physical and psychological risks to the surrogate mother from the pregnancy and the effect of the surrogate pregnancy on the surrogate mother's existing family (especially her husband, if she has one). Care must be taken to screen the surrogate mother for various conditions related to health in pregnancy and both the commissioning couple and the surrogate mother must be screened for HIV and hepatitis B.

Whether or not the couple and the surrogate mother should meet or remain anonymous is another area of concern; to remain anonymous may protect the two parties involved

from further distress should problems arise. The knowledge that the child may be able to discover its natural parents (because it will be legally adopted) is also important and may dissuade many from going through with the process. The current practise is for openness with generally a considerable amount of contact between the couple and the surrogate.

Our response

We must respond in at least two ways to the issue; we must look at the overall problem and we must look at the problem in a personal context. Is it ever right or correct to use surrogacy, and would it be right for me to use it to help a couple to have a baby and would it be right for me to use it myself to have a baby?

With the ethical and legal concerns that must be clearly understood by both parties, it is difficult to see how the process can be entertained without someone getting hurt. While 'getting hurt' may be acceptable as an inevitable consequence of living in a fallen world, we must accept some responsibility for the child who may be born as a result of this arrangement, who will not have been consulted and whose rights must be proposed by someone. As physicians, aware of that responsibility, we should

Table 1: Possible indications for the use of surrogacy

Sound medical grounds	*Questionable and spurious grounds*
• Ovarian failure.	• Apareunia.
• Major uterine anomalies.	• Severe dyspareunia.
• Absent uterus.	• Unprepared for inconvenience of pregnancy.
• History of severe pregnancy-associated illnesses.	• Unwilling to conceive for social, psychological or financial reasons.
• History of oestrogen-dominent tumour.	
• History of severe medical disorders.	
• Severe Rhesus disease.	
• Recurrent miscarriage.	

Table 2: Summary of legal status of surrogacy

Surrogacy arrangements are not enforceable in law, are of themselves not illegal, and any commercial interest in the arrangement (by the commissioning couple), the surrogate or a third party agency) is illegal. The payment of reasonable expenses (loss of work, all treatment costs, child care etc) is permissible.

A child born as a result of surrogacy is the legal child of the surrogate mother but can, through a court order, be treated in law as the child of the commissioning couple. This court order needs to be arranged 6 weeks after and within 6 months of the birth of the child. At that time, the child must be living with the commissioning couple, and the home must be in the UK. The surrogate must be in complete agreement with the order.

If the eggs and/or sperm (gametes) used in the treatment of the surrogate mother, then those gametes ought to be considered as coming from a donor, and the same precautions taken as with donor eggs or sperm.

perform that task if no one else will. It may be better to avoid the situation completely by not permitting the arrangement to proceed rather than be unsure about this aspect.

The debate which exists about the use of donor sperm by or for Christians has some parallels here. Many of the arguments on both sides of the debate related to donor sperm could be applied to the use of surrogacy. Most doctors (including any Christian doctors I have spoken to) would not favour the use of surrogacy.[1,3]

Some of the arguments which related to the use of donor sperm were aired in the Christian Medical Fellowship magazine *In the Service of Medicine* in the past. Those who objected to the use of donor sperm did so on the basis of a contravention of the spirit of Scripture, as it was considered to be close to adultery and to interfere in the bond of 'one flesh' referred to in Scripture (Gen 2:24; Eph 5:31).[8] It would also cause ethical and social dilemmas as it would mean that someone had to judge another's suitability for parenthood, the whole area of confidentiality was very complex and there was the risk of passing on a genetic disorder. The proponents of its use suggested that it did not represent adultery as there was no sexual intercourse and no impingement on the emotional and spiritual relationship between man and woman.[9] While not denying the existence of the other problems referred to, the proponents felt they were not insurmountable.

Exchange 'surrogacy' for 'donor insemination' and the arguments are very similar to those being applied to surrogacy. But, the reaction to surrogacy is much stronger and the opposition to it more deep. This must be related to the very different implications for a woman if she does agree to being a surrogate mother, considering all she must take on.

To answer the original questions of this section: in principle, I believe that there may be occasions where the option of surrogacy may be the only option for a couple wishing for their own (genetic) child – or even partly their own. I believe that the only way this should be carried out is by the maintenance of strict anonymity between the surrogate mother and the commissioning couple. A child born of such an arrangement is at least as likely to be nurtured and loved as many children born in more normal circumstances.

In practice, however, I believe it must be extremely difficult to give full and adequate counselling to all parties concerned; there would be major difficulties with anonymity (particularly when it came to the court order for adoption) and I would conclude that surrogacy should not generally be practised or available as part of the service we offer to couples who cannot have their own children.

Summary

One eminent writer on the Christian response to IVF and its related techniques has said 'It is certain that . . . There will be no escape from surrogate motherhood'.[10] Patients will continue to push to find a way for them to resolve their infertility and the option of surrogacy is one resolution. The ethical problems are enormous and the legal constraints quite tough. The potential for the major difficulties that have been outlined above. These factors carry the implication that entry into such treatment is fraught with problems and in general, I believe, best avoided.

David Cahill
Clinical Research Fellow
Obstetrics and Gynaecology, Bristol

References
1 Surrogacy Report. Appendix V to Annual Report of Council, BMA 1989-1990: 39-48 in BMJ 1990; 300: after 854.
2 Macnaughton M. Ethics and Reproduction. Am J Obstet Gynecol 1990; 162: 897-882.
3 Warnock Dame M. Report of the Committee of Inquiry into Human Fertilisation and Embryology. HMSO, London 1984.
4 Surrogacy Arrangements Act 1985. HMSO, London 1985.
5 The Human Fertilisation and Embryology Act 1990. HMSO, London 1990.
6 Genesis 2:18.
7 Genesis 1:28.
8 Manifold I. Artificial Insemination by Donor's semen – a Christian viewpoint. In the Service of Medicine 1982; 28:21-27
9 Stirrat G M. Artificial Insemination by Donor – a Christian Viewpoint. In the Service of Medicine 1983; 29:13-15.
10 Jones D G. Brave New People. IVP, Leicester 1984; p.185.

BMA *rethink over surrogate mothers*

Association allows help for childless couples as 'last resort'

By Chris Mihill,
Medical Correspondent

Surrogate pregnancies are acceptable as a last resort for infertile couples when other fertility treatments have failed, the British Medical Association said yesterday in a change of policy.

The BMA said doctors should advise patients about surrogacy if appropriate, and infertile couples should feel they can discuss the subject with health professionals without fear of recrimination or judgement.

Fleur Fisher, head of the BMA ethics division, said: 'Surrogacy is here to help infertile couples, and it is important that we recognise that this is an area of infertility management that we need to learn about. All parties need the best quality of clinical and counselling care that we can make available to them.'

However, the BMA said surrogacy contracts could not be enforced in law, and that such arrangements were fraught with problems. But in most cases it had looked at, the outcome had been positive.

The BMA originally advised doctors to have nothing to do with surrogacy, although later it told doctors they could help but that the two parties to the pregnancy should have as little contact as possible to lessen potential psychological problems.

The new advice, in a book for doctors and booklet for patients, says there are benefits from the surrogate mother and would-be parents supporting each other, and extended discussions between the parties can help prevent future problems arising.

Dr Fisher said there was anecdotal evidence that the number of surrogate births was increasing, as society became less judgemental, although no official figures were kept. The larger of the two voluntary agencies which set up surrogacy arrangements, COTS, estimates it has helped 150 pregnancies over the past four years, but other couples make their own arrangements.

> **The BMA said patients should feel they can discuss the subject with health professionals without fear of recrimination or judgement**

Dr Fisher said that if DIY surrogacy was agreed on – where the mother used her own eggs and sperm from the other woman's husband –

there was often little medical involvement and both sides missed out on counselling.

Some women denied their pregnancy was surrogate, for fear that the child would be taken into care.

In other cases, where IVF clinics were involved, there was formal psychological assessment and counselling. 'We want the same level of counselling and support as given by the IVF clinics to all people involved in surrogacy arrangements,' she said.

The report backs the outlawing of commercial surrogacy but says it is reasonable that the surrogate mother receives expenses of £7,000 to £10,000.

The BMA says the voluntary agencies which set up surrogacy arrangements should be more closely monitored for the quality of advice they provide for couples, and that there needs to be more research into the effects of such births on the surrogate mothers, the parents and the children.

Ann Somerville, the BMA's adviser on ethics and the law, said there had been cases in which handicapped babies had been rejected by the would-be parents or when the surrogate mother had refused to hand over the child.

'The whole procedure is fraught with problems from beginning to end.'

• *Changing Conceptions of Motherhood: the Practice of Surrogacy in Britain.* British Medical Association. £6.95.

© *The Guardian February, 1996*

Surrogacy

New NHS services for surrogate motherhood smack of state baby-farming. But, asks Polly Toynbee, can we condemn women for profiting from surrogacy?

It is an unsavoury business, surrogacy. However decorously it is presented, the basic fact is that a rich infertile couple pays a poor woman to bear their child. Almost always it is her own genetic child, conceived with a test-tube of the buyer's sperm, so the word 'surrogate' is a serious misnomer – the child is as much hers as any other. Now, occasionally, an embryo created from the egg and sperm of the couple may be implanted instead.

The law cannot prevent surrogacy. How do you ban women being impregnated by men they barely know? (It happens all the time.) How do you stop a man adopting his own genetic offspring, if the mother hands it over? The law is left on the sidelines, banning middlemen from profiteering, and somewhat arbitrarily fixing the maximum price paid to the mother at £10,000, describing the money euphemistically as 'costs' and 'compensation for loss of earnings'. For a mother on social security, that is a lot of money. Without mincing words, these babies are being bought and sold.

Usually it happens behind closed doors, but the British Medical Association reckons about 100 surrogate babies are born each year. Until it comes to the adoption hearing, the state has no involvement and even then often no one reveals what has passed. Some of these arrangements end in the bitter tears of women who regret giving away their babies, or the angry tears of would-be parents who have no legal redress if the surrogate changes her mind and keeps both baby and fee.

Now the National Health Service is to venture into these treacherous waters. The NHS will rent a womb and purchase a baby for you. It is cheaper, they say, than test-tubes. At this point what was a private, if unseemly, deal between individuals becomes the direct responsibility of all us tax-paying citizens. This is state baby-farming and the moral ground feels as if it shifts uneasily beneath our feet. But why should we be queasy at the state buying poor women's babies in our name? Why shouldn't the NHS let poor couples also exploit other poor women?

For a mother on social security, £10,000 is a lot of money. Without mincing words, these babies are being bought and sold

---

There is a dubious moral squeamishness at work here. We live in a society where many of the poor, by accident, bad luck, stupidity or incompetence, have no chance of participating in the ordinary quality of life of the great majority. There is, however, absolutely no sign that taxpayers are so morally shocked that they yearn to pay more in order to fund expensive new projects to rescue the poor from their benighted lives. On social security the only thing many have left to sell is their bodies. Some women turn to prostitution, a few to womb-renting. And why not, since we have nothing else to offer them?

By the same token, I see no valid moral argument why the poor should not sell their kidneys if they choose. Most healthy people can function perfectly well with one. The chance to earn a windfall of, say, £50,000, could make a real difference to their lives, and would seem a perfectly rational choice to make.

In fact kidney sale is a far better proposition than surrogacy, since the donors are unlikely to mourn their loss the way a mother may mourn her missing child. A hard-headed examination of the issues raised by surrogacy on the NHS may well lead down the path to NHS-purchased spare organs. It would save the lives of many kidney patients dying while they wait, and the livelihoods of the desperately poor. © *The Independent February, 1996*

Implications for the surrogate mother

Psychological aspects of surrogacy

Attachment to the foetus and baby
Although feelings of attachment to the foetus generally increase over the course of a pregnancy, it is normal for a woman's feelings to fluctuate. Prenatal feelings of attachment to the foetus have been found to be strongly related to feelings about the baby after the delivery. Thus a surrogate mother who develops strong attachment during pregnancy is likely to find it particularly difficult to relinquish the child. Whilst surrogate mothers appear to be more detached from their foetus than is usual, they may come to love the baby by the ninth month. Such an attachment is advantageous in that it is likely to discourage the woman from behaving in a way that would otherwise risk her health and that of the foetus. However, a surrogate mother's relationship with the child both during pregnancy and afterwards may well be very ambivalent. She might start by feeling good about the gesture she is making to the couple, but gradually experience a sense of conflict, apprehension or even guilt. These feelings could, at the time of the birth, result in her deciding to keep the child, despite entailing that she has to bring up a child she had not planned to keep. Even if she does relinquish the child, feelings of pain, anger and guilt might persist for a very long time, and be coupled with fears that the child was not being properly loved and cared for.

It is sometimes suggested that full surrogacy is preferable to partial surrogacy, because the surrogate will not have made a genetic contribution in the former case and so may feel less of a sense of loss on parting with the child. However, as people vary in their feelings about the importance of genetic relationships, this may not hold for all surrogate mothers. Also important may be the consideration that if the baby is genetically related to the surrogate mother, it may remind her of her own children and therefore make it harder for her to relinquish.

While the BMA acknowledges that there is very little systematic information on the experience of surrogacy, what little there is suggests that only a small proportion of surrogate mothers go so far as to retain the child. It is certainly a smaller proportion than those mothers who plan to release their child for adoption but change their mind when the baby is born.

Postnatal psychological reactions
The surrogate mother should be aware of the risk of postnatal depression, as well as the fact that experience of postnatal depression carries a risk of relapse with subsequent babies.

Women's risk of depressive illness is substantially increased after childbirth: rates of depression any time in the first year after delivery are in the order of 10-20%. The exact cause is undetermined, but it is not solely the result of hormonal influences. Vulnerability factors specific to postnatal depression include previous psychiatric history, lack of employment, housing problems, poor marital relations, lack of social and emotional support and little previous contact with babies. Women experiencing postnatal depression commonly feel inadequate, angry, helpless or hopeless. Experiences of depressed mood are likely to be exacerbated by economic privation, disturbed sleep and physical exhaustion. In cases of mild depression, simply allowing women to talk about their experience and feelings can be valuable in alleviating depression.

There are no data on the incidence of postnatal depression in surrogate mothers. Precipitating factors suggest that the risk of depression may be reduced for surrogate mothers who already have children of their own and who have partners able to provide support. However, given that many psychological factors thought to be important in the development of such depression relate to the woman's experience with her baby (for example, inability to cope, social isolation), it might be expected that surrogate mothers would be *less* vulnerable to postnatal depression. On the other hand, the surrogate mother has chosen to relinquish the baby, and therefore may experience the sort of emotional distress normally associated with perinatal loss. A small study of surrogate mothers found that 75% of women reported moderate or severe depression 'which included uncontrollable sobbing, sleep dysfunction, aching arms and difficulty interacting with other newborns' which lasted from 2 to 6 weeks. In one case the woman had to be hospitalised.

Surrogate mothers who suffer from postnatal depression may require less practical support than mothers who have a baby to deal with, but their need for psychological support is likely to be just as great. If depression persists, treatment or referral to a psychiatrist should be considered, particularly if the surrogate has children of her own.

• The above is an extract from *Changing Conceptions of Motherhood: The Practice of Surrogacy in Britain*, published by the British Medical Association.

© BMA
January, 1996

Three-parent families

How does it feel to be the child of a sperm donor? Last week, a couple anxious to have a baby asked for advice on the consequences of taking that route. Here we publish letters from our readers

After several desperate years of trying for a baby, my husband and I have recently been told, by a well-known UK fertility centre, that our only realistic hope of achieving a pregnancy is to use donor sperm. We are seriously considering this option, but we are very concerned about the possible consequences, mainly whether my husband will be able to feel the full array of paternal emotions towards the child and how will the child feel about its origins? We would be very interested to hear how other families have coped with this situation.

I am a 39-year-old woman with a two-year-old daughter and a happy marriage. After years of trying to conceive, we learnt that my husband was sterile and the only way we were to have a family would be to consider accepting the donor sperm route. This usually also entails taking hormones, assisted cycles, artificial insemination and more people than you might like knowing your business. Having always been convinced that nurture is a million times more important than nature, we committed ourselves to this option, traumatic and upsetting as it was for both of us.

Of course I had always dreamt of having my husband's baby and the hardest part was facing the fact that this was never to be. After four attempts at AID (artificial insemination using donor sperm), I became pregnant and both of us could not have been more delighted. From that moment onwards, it could not have mattered one jot about how I got pregnant and going through the pregnancy process together – scans, kicks, indigestion, emotions – served (as it does in many pregnancies) as my husband's apprenticeship for fatherhood. Our daughter was born and is very much loved by both of us.

There is no doubt that my husband is her father and because his involvement has been so conscious and considered, his commitment and care for her is more intense than many biological fathers'. Because of the closeness they have developed and time spent together, my daughter actually looks the image of my husband (apparently this is quite a common phenomenon) a fact remarked upon by our friends and even passers-by!

All I can say is that my husband not only feels the full array of paternal emotions towards our child but is very keen for us to have another now. We fully intend to let our children know about their origins as soon as possible and allow them to decide how they wish to respond to the facts.

The one area we have had a problem with is in deciding who to tell. When we first found out, we told immediate family and close friends, and now rather regret being so open, as people sometimes bring up this intensely personal subject when we now feel it irrelevant and none of their business.

Another unresolved area is how our children will cope with the information. Many children grow up without ever having known their true biological father. If our kids at a later date feel keen to locate their father – this is their prerogative. All we can do is love them and care for them now. We are very clear about one thing: their 'real father' is the man who talked to them in the womb, held my hand at the birth, changed nappies at 4am, makes bottles, takes his daughter swimming and will tell her the facts of life, not some anonymous medical student who ejaculated into a teacup.

Name and address withheld

Please don't consider me negative if I start by saying that I faced your dilemma and felt I didn't want to have a child who would be

unable to trace his/her natural parent, but that I wished I could. The decision was taken 12 years ago, and the circumstances were different. I've never had children, even though, as far as I know, I would be able to with a different partner. I'm now 42 and have been celibate for 10 years. The fact that I couldn't have children with my then-partner led to our break-up and a great deal of sadness.

I don't regret the decision I took, but wished I could have taken different ones. I still couldn't go through with it, but if you can, then do.

Veda Dovaston
Petersfield, Hampshire.

Having had two children through donor insemination, we'd like to encourage you to talk directly to people who have considered the same issues as you. We are members of the Donor Insemination Network, which has a newsletter and regular conferences; the next is in London on March 1. Write to DI Network, PO Box 265, Sheffield, S3 7YX or telephone 0181 245 4369.

H Pugh and K Hill,
London N15

Why are you 'desperate' for a baby? Could your 'desperation' be influenced by media accounts of other 'desperate' couples and their 'miracle' babies? Or by none-too-subtle hints from other people that you are somehow incomplete without children? Are you sure you haven't let yourselves become so obsessed with your 'problem' that you've given too little thought to what else life might have to offer?

By any standards, childlessness is a very minor hardship: you don't have to have children to lead full and rewarding lives. Your misgivings about following the clinic's suggestion are well founded. For the child's sake as well as your own, the rule must be: if in doubt, don't.

Root Cartwright, Chairman,
British Organisation of Non-Parents,
BM Box 5866,
London WC1N 3XX

Be positive! You have three possible options. To remain childless, to adopt a child that will inherit none of your genes, or to have a child with donor sperm that will inherit 50 per cent of your genes and 100 per cent of its parents' nurturing. Surely

this is the best solution. Do not waste your emotions on agonising over hypothetical issues, but channel all your love into the small miracle of a baby. If, later on, explanations are necessary, the child can be made to feel special that you went to so much trouble to give it life. Good luck.

Naomi Salter,
Lymington, Hants

You do not say what treatment you have had to date. There is a new treatment for male infertility known as ICSI which is proving highly successful for many couples. Have you been offered this treatment? If you have and it has failed, then donor insemination probably is your last option.

If you have not already done so, join ISSUE (the address will be available at your fertility clinic) and obtain from them a list of the centres offering ICSI. You might also benefit from talking to one of their counsellors.

Name and address withheld
© *The Guardian*
February, 1997

Implications for the intended parents

Psychological aspects of surrogacy

In making the decision to proceed with surrogacy, the intended parents face a great deal of uncertainty. They might feel guilt about the arrangement, coupled with a worry that, however rare in practice, the child will not be relinquished. They may be concerned with uncertainty about the adoption or parental orders process. They might worry about their reaction to the child being born handicapped; and, with partial surrogacy, they may harbour doubts that the child's parentage is as claimed. They might also fear that information about the arrangement will fall into the wrong

hands. They may even come to regard the child not as a release from their childlessness, but as a continuing reminder of their inability to produce a child without help.

Attachment to the foetus or baby

Some intended parents may be concerned that they will not be able to accept the child as their own. If

partial surrogacy is used, the woman, in particular, might be concerned that she will not become attached to the child, and that she will find it difficult to accept the biological child of her partner and another woman. However, it is clear that successful attachment relationships form between parents and children even when parents have no genetic relationship with the child and are not present immediately after delivery. Attachment is not something that is only formed during a critical period after delivery, but develops gradually over a period of time. The intended parents have the advantage over adoptive parents of having nine months in which to prepare for the baby's appearance.

The importance of early interactions and continuity of parenting should not, however, be underestimated. Babies learn very fast: for example, within a few days of birth they have learned the particular way in which they are held when fed, and can anticipate the breast or bottle as soon as they are held in this way. They quickly learn to distinguish their mother's face from another's and, if breast fed, to recognise the smell of her milk. Whenever a baby is transferred to a different mother or parents, relationships will be disrupted, and the baby is likely to share its distress with its new parents. These effects are probably transient, but all attempts should be made to reduce the distress caused to the baby, in view of its dependence on adults. Thus, it is likely to be beneficial for the baby to establish contact with the intended parents as soon as possible after delivery.

Breast feeding has advantages for the baby's physical health, but the relationship between breast feeding and the development of attachment between mother and baby is not clear. Whilst there is some suggestion that breast feeding immediately after delivery leads to stronger bonding, this does not necessarily imply that bonding will occur if the surrogate mother wishes to feed the child. The intended mother should be aware that it may be possible for her to establish breast feeding with the baby.

Psychological reactions
An intended mother who lacks experience with babies may have to deal with the additional belief that the 'natural' mother could have cared for the baby better than she is able to do. Moreover, psychosocial factors implicated in postnatal depression (lack of social and emotional support, social isolation) may equally apply to women who have to care for babies after adoption or surrogacy. An intended mother may have a small risk of developing depression after receiving the child. It has been estimated that about 1 in 2000

women experiences post-adoptive depression.

Intended parents should be aware that it is not unusual for marital satisfaction to decline in some respects after the birth of a baby. Should marital problems be experienced, this should not necessarily be attributed to the surrogacy arrangement.

Anonymity and telling the child
One question which all intended parents have to deal with is whether to tell their child of his or her origins. Most people who choose surrogacy report that they have decided to explain the circumstances of the conception and birth to their child. If parents decide not to tell, they face a number of difficulties. Surrogacy is thought to be difficult to conceal from others, and if other people know about the arrangement, then the child may find out from them (whether deliberately or inadvertently). The experience of learning in this way, and the discovery of deception by his or her parents may be very distressing for a child. Such an experience may have long-term implications for the parent-child relationship. Even if a child does not discover in this way, a lack of openness may mean that the

One question which all intended parents have to deal with is whether to tell their child of his or her origins

parents have difficulty in communicating with their child on related topics – sex, contraception, fertility, genetic and family relationships, and family health problems. Such communication difficulties may lead the child to suspect that he or she is unusual, but discourage the child from trying to discuss these issues with his or her parents. Thus, in addition to general reasons for encouraging honesty with children, it may not be feasible, or in the child's long-term interests, for the truth to be withheld. The intended parents should also be aware that at 18 a person has a legal right to discover the identity of his or her surrogate mother.

Adoptive parents can use information about their child's birth mother to aid the process of telling the child. Parents with children conceived by donor insemination comment on the difficulty of talking in the absence of any information about the genetic father. An information profile on the surrogate mother might, therefore, be helpful in enabling parents to tell their child of her or his origins. Keeping the surrogate mother informed of the child's progress via reports may both ease any grief and provide recognition of her help. The BMA has been told by one of the self-help surrogacy support groups that arrangements which they foster on a non-commercial basis are often undertaken with open contact between all the parties, before and after birth, with a positive outcome for all. However, there has been no scientific examination of the psychological implications of anonymity or personal contact for parents or children involved in surrogacy arrangements. What is important, therefore, is that the surrogate mother and intended parents agree on a level of contact which they feel is appropriate for them.

• The above is an extract from *Changing Conceptions of Motherhood: The Practice of Surrogacy in Britain*, published by the British Medical Association. See page 39 for address details.

Lesbian Britain is baby booming

Fertility clinics are fuelling a lesbian baby boom which is challenging traditional values by creating a new class of two-mother families, researchers have found, writes Lois Rogers.

Hundreds of lesbian couples are having babies by artificial insemination and bringing up children without any other male involvement. More than half the women being treated at some fertility clinics are lesbians.

Many more are obtaining donor sperm from friends or by advertising for biological fathers. One lesbian primary school teacher said she and her lover received 40 serious responses – many from heterosexual men – to adverts for a 'no-strings' donor. Others say they want male role models for their children and have created non-sexual bonds with men who have fathered children. In some cases, the man has fathered children for both women in a lesbian relationship.

Experts say the rise in lesbian motherhood can be attributed to growing acceptance of homo-sexuality and greater willingness by fertility clinics to offer treatment. The Pregnancy Advisory Service in London now provides donor insemination for 100 women a month, of whom up to 60 are lesbians. The Bridge Fertility Centre in London estimated that a fifth of its clients for inseminations were lesbians. Other clinics confirmed a steady flow of lesbians who are open about their sexuality.

Hundreds of lesbian couples are having babies by artificial insemination and bringing up children without any other male involvement

---

Paula, a 37-year-old Midland social worker, has a 3-month-old daughter by sperm from a homosexual friend. Her girlfriend, Liz, is due to give birth this week to a child fathered by the same man.

'We wanted to share the load of being a mother,' said Paula. 'We are a family planning our future together, and we are doing this whole thing with the donor. It was crucial to me for there to be a father figure because I lost my own father when I was young.'

The trend has provoked concern among traditionalists. Valerie Riches, of Family and Youth Concern, a pressure group, said: 'Most people's gut reaction would be that this is wrong. Not enough thought is being given to what it must be like for children to grow up in situations where unnatural practices are taking place.'

This summer, for the first time, London's gay pride festival, which regularly attracts 150,000 people, is providing facilities for families. Lisa Saffron, who left her husband and founded a lesbian family with her girlfriend, is credited with opening the floodgates with her book *Challenging Conceptions: Planning a Family by Self-Insemination*, published three years ago.

Social researchers say children brought up by lesbians are emotion-ally healthy and well adjusted.

The other woman

For childless couples, a surrogate mother can seem the answer to all their prayers. But is she? Owen Bowcott talks to women who have seen it from both sides

Last week fertility experts revealed that 51-year-old Edith Jones, a grandmother from Darlington, is to become the first British woman to give birth to her own grandchild. Or grandchildren. Jones has had two embryos – grown from her daughter Suzanne's ova and son-in-law Chris' sperm – implanted in her womb. 'The moment the babies are born, I want to hand them over to Suzanne and Chris,' she said. 'I just want to see their faces when they hold them for the first time.'

Surrogate motherhood has come a long way since, in 1985, Kim Cotton caused shock and moral uncertainty by handing over her child to an American couple for £6,500.

These days Cotton, now aged 39, feels uneasy about what happened – but only because she knows how much better the procedure can be. 'That was arranged through an American agency. It was a disgusting surrogacy, even though I was happy with it at the time.'

She regrets that she had never met the couple beforehand and has not seen the child since. Known publicly as Baby Cotton, her daughter is now aged 11 and believed to be living in the States. 'You should always know who the couple are and keep in contact,' she says now – advice given to all those who contact her support group, Childlessness Overcome Through Surrogacy (C.O.T.S.).

Attitudes, she agrees, are changing. It was recently revealed that an NHS district authority had paid for surrogacy treatment for the first time and Cotton believes: 'Recognition that infertility is such a large problem has altered public opinion.'

The sea change in medical opinion came earlier this year when the British Medical Association (BMA), which once advised doctors to 'have no involvement with surrogacy', issued a revised guidance leaflet entitled *Changing Conceptions Of Motherhood*. The blanket BMA ban disappeared, replaced by a willingness to help tackle the myriad problems raised by the 'separation of maternity from social motherhood'. Among the BMA's areas of concern are lack of information about legal and emotional difficulties, and lack of psychological support for both parties after birth.

A clearer legal framework has helped smooth the way. Under the 1985 Surrogacy Act, commercial agencies were banned from profiting from surrogate agreements. The 1990 Human Fertilisation and Embryology Act required all infertility centres to be licensed and introduced fast-track procedures for legal adoption of surrogate babies.

The woman who gives birth is still legally the mother until adoption is confirmed. 'Surrogacy contracts are unenforceable,' a spokeswoman for the Human Fertilisation and Embryo Authority says, 'so there's a six-week delay before legal proceedings. The surrogate mother can change her mind and keep the child, even if she is genetically unrelated.'

The surrogate mother

Susan Bowser had no problem handing over the baby to whom she gave birth last August. The morning Angus arrived, she walked out of Doncaster Royal Infirmary and went

straight home; her medical file was even stamped 'Surrogate Mother,' 'Right from the moment I was pregnant, as far as I was concerned, he wasn't mine.'

The couple on whose behalf she had carried Angus stayed in hospital with him for the night. 'They didn't know one end from the other,' she recalls. 'They had to be shown how to bath and feed him.'

Surrogate motherhood runs in Bowser's family. Thirty years ago, one of her aunts became pregnant in order to provide a child for another aunt. 'One aunt had five children, but her sister couldn't have any – so she gave one to her. With that background, my family could understand my decision.'

Having had four children, Bowser, 32, is committed to helping those who cannot have families on their own. The idea occurred when she was carrying her second baby. 'I read an article about Kim Cotton, the first surrogate mother, and it seemed a wonderful thing to do.'

Bowser is in fact Angus' genetic mother. The previously childless couple for whom she carried him had wanted to implant in her their own test-tube-fertilised embryo, so that the woman, who'd had a hysterectomy and so couldn't carry a baby herself, would have been the genetic mother. But the eggs didn't take.

The couple had problems affording repeat operations: 'Some tests could be £800 each. So after that it was artificial insemination, his sperm and my egg.'

Syringes and equipment provided by the surrogacy support group C.O.T.S. eventually succeeded in making Bowser pregnant. She was paid expenses, including time taken off from her work at a factory, trips to the London clinic and maternity clothes. Total bill around £9,000.

'I saw Angus on Sunday for the first time since he was born. We had gone out for a meal with his adoptive parents. As we were paying the bill, I held him – and it was like I was handling someone else's baby.

'The couple said he had brought them so much joy. The mother looks much younger. They've asked me to do it again and I have said I will.'

The would-be mother

Four attempts have already been made at implanting in Anji Loman Field's womb embryos fertilised in a test-tube. The last one left her pregnant for just one day before she lost what could have become her first child.

'That was particularly cruel,' she says. 'We will probably have one more go, but if that does not take, we may opt for surrogacy.'

The couple's GP has said she will support their bid for surrogacy. If it goes ahead, Loman Field says, she will try to think of the process as 'rent-a-womb'. 'We can produce both eggs and sperm. We just want someone to carry a baby for us.'

Among the BMA's areas of concern are lack of information about legal and emotional difficulties, and lack of psychological support for both parties after birth

---

Anji, a television scriptwriter, aged 37, and her partner David, 39, a TV engineer, have considered asking a member of their families or a friend to act as surrogate mother. But no obvious candidate comes to mind. 'My sister has two children but had so many problems with her pregnancy. My mother is 65. Most of my friends have been through childbirth recently and are worn out. So it's probably going to have to be done through an agency.'

Loman Field cannot carry a child because she has a rare condition in which antibodies in her blood attack sperm. 'If I could market the antibodies for women as a contraceptive, I could make a fortune.'

At £800 for each IVF treatment, costs can be a disincentive, but attitudes are changing. 'Our last attempt was paid for on the NHS.'

The couple are very close to accepting surrogacy as the only remaining treatment open to them and are on the point of contacting a surrogacy support group. 'It's either that or place an advert saying: *Wanted: 26-year-old with complete family and womb to rent'*.

Loman Field hopes that, if they do opt for surrogacy, she will be able to be the genetic mother, with her egg implanted in a host mother. She would feel uneasy about her partner's sperm fertilising the surrogate's egg. 'I would have to think much harder about that.'

The parents

In 1984, 20-year-old Debbie Riley went into hospital for a hysterectomy to prevent cancer spreading from her womb. Ten years later, she arrived home with triplets.

Unable to carry a child because of the earlier surgery, surrogacy was the only way in while Riley, now 32, could become a mother. She and her husband, Eddy, also 32, could produce embryos through in-vitro fertilisation, but another woman was needed for the actual pregnancy.

After five years of treatment costing nearly £20,000, it was Debbie's sister-in-law, Dawn Spindler, who eventually agreed to act as surrogate mother. In mid-July 1993, she had three embryos implanted in her womb at AMI Park Hospital in Nottingham. The babies, Ben, Lauren and Matthew, were born in February 1994, three months premature and by Caesarean.

'It's been great, there have been no problems at all,' Riley insists, 'though it's hard work with the children. Three's a handful.'

Her husband is still awestruck at Dawn's generosity. 'She went through an awful lot having triplets. She already had children of her own and it took 12 months out of her life.

'We have decided to tell the children when they grow up. We've kept newspaper cuttings and videos of the news. It has had some bad press, but I'm totally for surrogacy. If everybody who wanted a baby had to go through what we did, there would hardly be any kids in the world. It's a long and inefficient process – but it's worth it in the end.'

© The Guardian
April, 1996

Brave new frontier?

Furore over the surrogate mother carrying babies for two sets of parents at the same time

A surrogate mother is to give birth to two babies by different sets of parents.

The 35-year-old Italian is believed to be the first woman in the world to be implanted with embryos from separate couples.

After she gives birth in September, blood tests will determine which of the pseudo-twins belongs to which parents.

The arrangement has caused an outcry in Italy, with health minister Rosy Bindi saying: 'We have crossed unimaginable boundaries. We need new international legislation. Man can no longer be allowed to be "Master of Life".'

The Vatican said: 'This is a further disastrous step forward to horrendous madness in the name of "assisted creation".'

The surrogacy of such pseudo-twins is not allowed in Britain, the Human Fertilisation and Embryology Authority said yesterday. 'It could lead to uncertainty about a child's parentage,' said Carol Perkins of the authority. 'One has to ask about the motivation of those carrying out this kind of procedure and the host surrogate carrying two embryos.'

But gynaecologist Pasquale Bilotta defended his work, saying two married women desperate to have children had begged him in tears for help. 'Could I possibly have denied them?' he asked.

One, aged 27, from Rome, had lost a baby and had her uterus removed. The other, aged 32 and from southern Italy, was unable to conceive because a heart complaint prevented her risking the stress of pregnancy.

The two couples are not being identified and surrogate mother is being named only as Angela. She has two children of her own, aged eight and ten.

From Ronald Singleton in Rome

Professor Bilotta, who runs the Alma Res Infertility Centre in Rome, said there was a shortage of surrogate mothers in Italy, where surrogacy is banned. He carried out his work on the three women in a Swiss clinic.

'Angela's babies are in splendid condition and should arrive in September,' he said.

'I synchronised the ovulation of all three women and at the precisely correct moment implanted the embryos. Each is in a separate sac and will not interfere with each other.

'This has broken a brave new frontier. Motherhood is the most beautiful thing in life. We are all delighted.' Angela said: 'I am giving infinite happiness to four people desperately needing children.

'Only a mother and certainly not theorists will understand my euphoria. My husband and my children know what I am doing and they're very happy.

'I am a devoted, practising Catholic. I have no problem with my conscience even though I know my church is wholly against what I am doing.

'I do not know the couples I am helping and never will. I will not even be able to see the children when they are born. They will be consigned to their parents immediately.

'On that day I shall of course be very sad in a certain way.

'Critics say I am simply a loveless "container." I read one headline, "One womb, two babies, five parents." I simply make my body at the disposition of others to make them happy.

'I do it not for a single penny, but for love. Mothers will understand me, for they know it is so beautiful to be a mother. God knows.'

Angela will return to the Swiss clinic for the birth.

The medical technique used by Professor Bilotta is standard practice. He uses in-vitro fertilisation (IVF), in which the woman's egg is fertilised by the man's sperm in a test-tube and developed to the stage where it can be implanted.

Two or more embryos are often implanted to maximise the changes of pregnancy – but belonging to the same parents, not different couples as in the Italian case.

Leading fertility specialist Peter Brinsden, medical director of Bourn Hall clinic near Cambridge, said there was no medical reason why two unrelated embryos should not be carried in the same womb.

'The mother feeds the baby from her blood supply, but the baby does not feed much back,' he said. 'The only obvious problems would be rhesus blood incompatibility, but that was probably checked for in advance of the pregnancy.

'Carrying twins slightly increases the risk of miscarriage and the risk to the mother, but otherwise the pregnancy is no more likely to have complications than one involving foetuses of the same genetic make-up.'

Dr Brinsden said that simple blood tests would establish the parentage of the babies after birth – 'It is a technique of chromosomal analysis widely used in legal cases where there is a dispute over paternity.'

However, he said, British law would not permit such an 'unusual' arrangement as the Italian 'twins' and he added: 'One does ask why anyone should want to do it.'

The timewarp twins with three mothers

It's a miracle, I'm overwhelmed by emotion says the woman

They were born 22 months apart and share three mothers. But Jennifer Gunther and her as-yet-unnamed baby brother are twins.

They were conceived from the same batch of frozen eggs using IVF techniques and carried by volunteer mothers in what is believed to be a world first.

Yesterday, the children's natural mother, Tricia Gunther, was almost lost for words after her dream family of a boy and a girl came true at last.

Beaming with delight as she cuddled her fair-haired son, 41-year-old Tricia, from Chester, said: 'It is a miracle. I can't put into words the overwhelming emotion I feel. It is perfect – I now have a boy and a girl. The feeling of holding your child and completing your family is just great.'

But what of the feelings of the women who carried the children during pregnancy? Both insist they are delighted for Tricia and her husband Julian, a college lecturer, and have no maternal feelings towards the two children.

Gaynor Crutchley, 31, who gave birth to the 7lb 11oz boy on Thursday and has three children of her own, said: 'He is beautiful. I am so happy for Tricia.'

She said of the birth: 'When the midwife asked who she should hand him to I pointed to Tricia and said, 'To the mother.' When I did hold him it was lovely but the maternal bond just wasn't there.

'Throughout the pregnancy it has been the same. It feels a bit weird but with this child my feelings have been quite different from when I had my own three.

'I don't feel as if I should be taking the baby home because no part of it has anything to do with my partner Cliff or me. If it had, that would be different.'

By Michael Seamark and Andrew Loudon

Her words echoed the emotions felt 22 months earlier by Teresa Finlay.

Teresa, who has a five-year-old son called Liam, said: 'It was like a job done. I was happy that Tricia had her baby and I felt I had done something to help someone, which made me feel good. The bond was never there for me either. It was always Tricia's baby.'

The twins were conceived in a test-tube seven years ago and deep frozen until volunteers could be found to carry them.

First Teresa, 31, from Connah's Quay, Flintshire, came forward after hearing how the Gunthers were desperate for a baby but were unable to have children. She has since become a friend of the family.

Nearly two years later Gaynor, who had answered the first appeal for surrogates, was approached and asked if she was still willing. Just before midnight on Thursday at the Countess of Chester Hospital, Jennifer's belated twin was born to complete the family. The news thrilled staff at Bourn Hall fertility clinic in Cambridgeshire, whose expertise made it possible.'

Medical director Peter Brinsden said: 'I am delighted that Mrs Gunther has been successful twice. Using embryos from the same batch with two different hosts makes this almost certainly unique in the world.'

Laws on surrogacy allow the natural parents to pay the host expenses such as travel costs, clothing and loss of earnings but not a fee for carrying the baby.

Legally the new baby belongs to Gaynor and her partner. As with Jennifer, the Gunthers now have to go through a fast-track adoption process for their son to obtain a birth certificate naming them as his parents.

SEE YOU IN 22 MONTHS TIME!

TWINS

KenPyne

Baby and surrogate grandmother 'fine'

By David Graves

Britain's first surrogate grandmother, who gave birth to her own grandchild because her daughter was unable to, is expected to leave hospital with the baby 'in a few days'.

Edith Jones gave birth to Caitlin by caesarean section and the child will be brought up by her daughter, Suzanne, 22, and husband, Christopher, 23.

Mrs Jones, 52, had been implanted with two embryos created from fertilised eggs from her daughter and son-in-law in a case which has concerned the Roman Catholic Church and fertility experts.

Both Mrs Jones and Caitlin, who weighed in at 5lb 3oz after the birth last Thursday, were said to be 'doing well' at Darlington Memorial Hospital yesterday.

A hospital spokesman said: 'There are no problems at all. This birth is being treated the same as any other.

'They should remain in hospital for a few days. No time has been fixed for when they will leave – just when they are ready.'

Mrs Jones, of Darlington, agreed to the surrogacy after her daughter, discovered she had no womb, although she was able to produce eggs normally.

Mrs Jones told a Sunday newspaper: 'She looked so small, so tiny that moment she was born. She looked gorgeous, really beautiful. She had that glow on her, a real rosy glow. And of course Suzanne couldn't stop crying.

'She had always said, "I don't think I'll cry Mam," but I knew she would. She was thanking me all the time and crying.'

Earlier this year, Mrs Jones had said: 'This baby will be genetically Suzanne and Chris's. All I am doing is lending them my body for nine months.'

Her daughter said: 'It was the most amazing feeling. I could hear a little cry and the doctor said, "Would you like to see what it is?"

'I couldn't believe it… a little girl. They took her to one side and checked her heart and breathing and then handed her to me. I just do not know how to say how wonderful I felt.'

The world's first surrogate grandmother, Pat Anthony, 56, from South Africa, gave birth to triplets for her daughter in 1987.

A spokesman for the Catholic Media Office said: 'This situation technically makes both the natural mother and the child of the same generation. It will surely cause considerable confusion to both children.'

Grandfather defends surrogate motherhood

By Will Bennett

The husband of the British woman who gave birth to her own granddaughter has rejected criticism of her by a Vatican newspaper.

L'Osservatore Romano said in an editorial yesterday that Edith Jones 'went against the law of creation as established by God' by deciding to carry her daughter's baby.

Mrs Jones, 52, gave birth to Caitlin in Darlington, Co. Durham, last Thursday because her daughter, Suzanne Langston, was born without a womb.

The baby was conceived by in-vitro fertilisation using eggs and sperm from Mrs Langston, 22, and her husband, Chris, 23, and then implanted into her grandmother's womb.

The Vatican newspaper continued: 'Above all else it is human dignity which is injured.'

But Mrs Jones's husband Trevor said last night: 'Of course everyone must have their own opinion on these matters but I would see nothing wrong with bringing such a beautiful baby into the world.

'Modern medicine made her possible and it was Suzanne's only chance of motherhood. This has been the right thing for our family.'

Dead husband is to father twins

As a woman is fertilised by her late partner's sperm, experts say the law is confused, writes Liz Hunt

A woman is expecting twins following a controversial form of fertility treatment which used sperm from her husband extracted before he died of cancer.

The use of posthumous frozen sperm after cancer treatment is well established, but success rates are low. Scientists say that a treatment, known as ICSI (intracytoplasmic sperm injection), in which sperm is injected directly into the egg, offers a far greater chance of a viable pregnancy in these cases.

The case, reported in the *British Medical Journal*, comes as Diane Blood, whose battle to have her dead husband's child has won widespread support of doctors and the public, announced she will take her case to the Court of Appeal on Monday. Mrs Blood, 31, whose husband slipped into a coma and died of meningitis before giving written permission for his sperm to be used, is challenging a ruling by the Human Fertilisation and Embryology Authority (HFEA) – subsequently upheld by the High Court – not to let her have fertility treatment here or abroad.

Mrs Blood's father, Michael McMahon, yesterday said his daughter had been advised by lawyers that she had a good legal case. She will be claiming the rulings were unreasonable, and that her rights under European law superseded British legal restrictions. She will also argue that when the sperm sample was taken from her husband he was still alive, and written consent should not have been necessary. Mr McMahon said: 'She is very, very optimistic now, but at the same time she's terrified of losing at this stage. It means so much to her.'

Doctors and scientists from London, Swansea, and Tyne and Wear, involved in the twin pregnancy in the 36-year-old woman whose husband died of testicular cancer, say that a comparison of this and the Blood case shows the 'limitations' of the law as it stands.

They say that sperm collected from an unconscious man – which the HFEA permits – cannot ever be used for treatment unless he recovers. Written consent is needed prior to use of the sperm in fertility treatments.

> **The case comes as Diane Blood, whose battle to have her dead husband's child has won widespread support of doctors and the public**

'As shown by our case, the HFEA is not opposed to posthumous assisted reproduction provided written consent is obtained. But death is seldom convenient,' the doctors write.

'The comparison of the two cases shows the limitation of the current law; it is conveniently applicable in a chronic illness but not so in an acute illness. Such inflexibility is germane to neither the human condition nor a rapid changing medical field.'

In the same issue of the *BMJ*, Professor Sir Douglas Black, former chief scientist in the Department of Health 1973-77, describes the decision to refuse Mrs Blood treatment, as 'corporate tyranny'.

He writes: 'It seems to me that this is a case in which the distress and hardship to an individual are glaringly obvious and the value to society . . . minimal. That view presupposes that legal and ethical principles are contingent, and not absolutes that need to be defended at whatever cost to actual living people.
© *The Independent*
January, 1997

In-vitro fertilisation (IVF)

Information from the Human Fertilisation & Embryology Authority (HFEA)

Introduction

IVF or 'in-vitro fertilisation' means fertilisation outside the body. It is a method which has helped many women have babies and first came to public notice in 1978 with the birth of the first so-called test-tube baby, Louise Brown. Since then about 70 clinics have been set up in the UK to offer IVF treatment. All IVF treatment clinics in the UK are monitored and licensed by the Human Fertilisation and Embryology Authority (HFEA), which is a public body set up by an Act of Parliament.

Briefly, IVF involves the collection of eggs and sperm which are mixed outside the woman's body in a culture dish or test-tube. Any resulting embryos are left to grow for about a day to check that they are developing normally and then up to three embryos are transferred into the woman's womb. If the treatment is successful, one or more embryos will implant in the lining of the womb and for each a foetus and placenta will develop. The woman will then be pregnant, just as if the woman had conceived normally. The procedures involved in IVF treatment are explained more fully in this article.

Who can benefit from IVF treatment?

IVF treatment is just one of the treatments for fertility problems. It can be offered as a treatment to women whose fallopian tubes are blocked or who have endometriosis*. It has been used successfully where infertility is unexplained. It can be helpful for couples who are infertile because of cervical mucus problems, or whose infertility is largely due to male factors. Some older women and

those whose eggs will not fertilise or who have had ovarian disease or surgery can be offered IVF using donated eggs.

Assessment and tests

If you and your partner have been trying to have a baby for at least two years without success, there are many tests which can be done to find out the reasons why. Your GP and consultant can then give you advice about the causes of your infertility and any possible treatments.

The IVF treatment clinic will conduct a first consultation with you where the causes of your fertility problem and the reasons for seeking treatment will be discussed. In all cases, before offering treatment, the doctor at a clinic will consider the welfare of any resulting child as well as of any other child who may be affected by the birth.

To find out which treatment offers the best chance to help you to have a child, several tests will be conducted to try to discover the cause of the problem. Many clinics prefer that their patients are referred to them by a GP or consultant so that the medical background of their fertility problems, including the results of such tests, is known.

A clinic may also do blood tests to check for immunity to German measles in the woman and for hepatitis B in both partners. Some

people, particularly those in risk groups, may be tested for HIV before having treatment.

If test show that the infertility is not apparently caused by faulty sperm or eggs, IVF treatment may be proposed to bring the sperm and eggs together outside the body to try to produce an embryo.

The IVF treatment procedure

There are several stages involved in IVF treatment. If your own eggs and your partner's sperm are to be used then the stages will be as follows:
* information will be provided
* you will be offered counselling
* you will be asked to give your consent to the use of your eggs, to your treatment and, if required, to disclose details about your treatment to your GP or to someone else who needs to know
* egg development will take place, with or without the administration of drugs
* egg collection will be carried out
* sperm collection will take place
* fertilisation will take place in-vitro
* up to 3 embryos will be transferred to your womb.

However, if it is discovered that either you or your partner is not producing fertile eggs or sperm, or if one of you carries an inherited disease, then using eggs or sperm donated by another person may be suggested. If you are to receive treatment with donated sperm, sperm collection will not take place. If you are receiving donated eggs then egg development and collection will be omitted but you may have to take drugs in preparation for embryo transfer.

Counselling

There are many considerations to be taken into account when deciding on fertility treatment. To help you, clinics are required by law to offer counselling before you consent to treatment. This counselling is different from the processes of receiving information, professional advice and assessment. It provides an opportunity to talk with an impartial person about the implications of the proposed treatment, for you, your family and any children born as a result. Support counselling, to give emotional support at times of particular stress, and therapeutic counselling should also be available.

Consent

There are three types of consent involved in IVF treatment:

1. Consent to use and storage

The law requires that you and your partner give written consent to the use and storage of your eggs or sperm and of any embryos produced. This consent is given on a form issued by the HFEA to the clinic.

Each partner in a couple must give separate consent to the use of their own eggs or sperm and their consent must be 'informed'. This means that the clinic must have provided information about the process and implications of IVF treatment and of storage. You must also be offered counselling about these implications. You or your partner can vary or withdraw consent to the use of eggs or sperm, or to the use of an embryo unless the embryo has already been used in treatment services or for research.

The separate consents to use and storage given by the man and woman (whether donors or not) providing eggs and sperm to be used together must be compatible.

If you are having IVF using donated sperm, your partner will not be asked to give this consent. The sperm donor will have given the necessary consent. Similarly, if donated eggs are used, the egg donor will give consent to use, not the woman receiving treatment.

2. Consent to treatment

You will be asked by the clinic to give written consent to your fertility treatment, such as egg retrieval and the transfer of a specified number of embryos into your womb. If donated sperm or donated eggs are used you will be asked to give consent to treatment using these and to embryo transfer.

3. Consent to disclosure of identifying information

Finally, the law requires that before a clinic can tell your GP or someone else who may need to know about your IVF treatment, your written consent to disclose identifying information must be obtained. You may wish to consider what information you wish to allow to be disclosed and to whom.

Egg development and drugs

Normally, every month a woman's ovaries develop several eggs but only one of these becomes fully mature. This egg is released into the fallopian tube where it may be fertilised following intercourse. For IVF, egg collection involves a small operation, so many clinics prefer to try to collect more than one egg at a time. To do this they give the woman hormone drugs. These cause the ovaries to mature several eggs in one monthly cycle which can be collected at one time. The embryos resulting from these eggs can be used in treatment that same month, or can be stored frozen for treatment later. Some clinics prefer not to use these drugs but collect the one or occasionally two eggs normally produced in a monthly cycle.

If drugs containing hormones are given, they will usually be of three types:
- a nasal spray or an injection given every day throughout the 28-day cycle. These drugs suppress the hormones produced by a woman in a normal menstrual cycle and enable greater control over when the eggs are produced;

- an injection given once a day for the first half of the cycle, or tablets to be taken. The injections or tablets are hormones which

naturally stimulate the ovaries, but which are given so that more than one egg develops. These are known as superovulatory drugs;

- when the ultrasound scanning and/or hormone measurements show that an adequate number of eggs are maturing, a final hormone injection is given which completes the maturing process. This injection must be carefully timed 34-38 hours before collection so that the eggs will be mature but will not have left the ovary.

Some of the drugs involved in an IVF cycle can be taken as tablets but many have to be given by injection. Clinics may give the daily injections themselves or they my arrange for a GP or local hospital to give them. Often this may cause some inconvenience. Sometimes training may be given so that the injections can be self-administered.

Further information

Information and advice about fertility treatment is available from a GP or consultant, the clinician, nurses and counsellor at a clinic. Each clinic produces its own patient information describing the services available and explaining what is involved in treatment.

Information on egg donation is available from NEEDS (St Mary's Hospital, Whitworth Park, Manchester M13 0JH. Telephone: 0161 276 6000 Fax: 0161 224 0957).

A disease in which tissue identical to the endometrical lining of the womb grows in the interior of the abdomen. Every month blood flows from this misplaced tissue, into the pelvic cavity, creating scar tissue that affects fertility.

- The above is an extract from a leaflet called *In-vitro fertilisation (IVF)*, produced by the Human Fertilisation & Embryology Authority. See page 39 for address details.

© Human Fertilisation & Embryology Authority (HFEA)
January, 1995

Ethical problems of infertility treatment

About one in seven couples finds difficulty conceiving children. The reasons are varied and there may be a combination of factors.

When a couple is looking forward to starting a family, their apparent inability comes as a great disappointment and frustration. Often it is a secret, lonely pain

Solutions and dilemmas

Many couples experience only a temporary delay in conceiving and children will arrive eventually. For others more help is needed and a doctor may refer the couple to an infertility clinic for diagnosis and/or help. This can take a number of forms. It may be the man who needs help in improving a low sperm-count. The woman may need drug treatment or surgery. But it is not uncommon for tests to reveal no apparent cause at all.

The treatment may in itself be a source of tension for the couple – temperature charts will not do anything for the spontaneity of love-making! And every month, the couple will be waiting on tenterhooks to see whether, this time, the woman is pregnant.

Unless medical advice indicates treatment should stop, the couple themselves must decide where to draw the line. In addition to the emotional tension and the discomfort involved, there are treatments which pose a number of ethical dilemmas. This article is designed to help you to think through these problems.

Could we use a donor?

For decades donated sperm has been used to help some couples have children in a technique called Artificial Insemination by Donor (AID). This may be offered to a couple where the woman's cervix is 'hostile' to the man's sperm or if the man's sperm are not viable. The sperm is introduced into the woman's womb through a tiny tube and conception takes place in the normal way. However, AID presents difficulties for the couple. The child will be biologically parented by the mother and an anonymous stranger.

Problems with using AID

– Literal adultery has not occurred but the child is conceived outside the marriage bond.
– AID may not be satisfactory to both partners and could cause tension and division between them.
– The parents may maintain the secret of the child's origin, so denying the child the right to fundamental information about his/her existence.
– Or the child must live with the knowledge that the father may never be known, and that the nurturing parents deliberately involved a third party to create pregnancy.

For these reasons most Christians find AID unacceptable.

A procedure which is more acceptable is AIH – Artificial

Insemination by Husband. The procedure is the same with the sperm being donated by the husband. This allows the natural conception of the couple's child and overcomes many of the ethical problems discussed above. This treatment is, of course, only relevant where the husband's sperm are viable.

What is IVF?

When other treatments have failed, some couples may be recommended to undergo in-vitro fertilisation (IVF). This involves bringing together the sperm and egg outside the body, allowing conception to take place and inserting the embryos in the woman's womb.

'In-vitro' literally means 'in glass'. In IVF fertilisation occurs in a laboratory

Problems with IVF

Spare embryos – the woman's ovary is usually stimulated to produce a number of eggs at once. After fertilisation around three or four will be selected to continue development in the womb (it is hoped at least one will result in a successful pregnancy). However, this leaves the remaining embryos unused. These tiny human beings may be frozen, thrown away, or used for research.

If two or more of the selected embryos successfully implant in the womb the couple may be offered a procedure known as selective reduction. This allows the couple to decide how many babies they want at one time. The unwanted embryos are selectively aborted and destroyed leaving the desired ones in place to continue developing.

Unknown risks – the technique is still relatively new and we cannot yet know for certain whether IVF in itself carries any risks for the children.

Mixed-up parents – donated eggs can be used where the woman cannot produce her own. IVF makes it possible for a child to be born to a couple to whom he/she is partially, or wholly, unrelated.

Quality control – doctors will, naturally, want to use only the most healthy embryos. But as tests develop to screen out undesirable embryos (by sex or hereditary abnormality), the expectation of producing only perfect children will increase. And in the process many 'second-rate' embryos will be destroyed.

Can IVF ever be right?

It is possible to perform IVF without creating 'spare embryos'. At least one clinic in Britain uses the woman's natural cycle, fertilises the one egg produced and replaces it in the womb. IVF does not have a very high success rate – around 10% – but using only one embryo does not seem to impair the chances of success. At other clinics the couple can always request that there are no 'spare embryos'.

If there are no 'spare embryos' and the husband and wife's sperm and egg are used, the ethical problems with IVF are significantly reduced.

GIFT and POST

There are many other techniques, for instance GIFT (gamete intrafallopian transfer) and POST (peritoneal oocyte and sperm transfer) which involve removing the woman's eggs, mixing them with sperm and then placing eggs and sperm in the woman's fallopian tubes (in the case of GIFT) or at the end of the tubes (POST) where fertilisation occurs. Neither of these two methods involves the creation of an embryo outside the woman's body; they avoid many of the ethical dilemmas of IVF. The problem of mixed-parentage can, however, still occur if the sperm and/or egg does not come from the couple.

The question of surrogacy

The idea of a woman intentionally bearing a child for another is not a new one. It is an age-old 'solution' for a childless couple – especially where an heir was required. However, surrogacy has taken on new dimensions in recent times.

Most commonly the surrogate mother is inseminated with the sperm of the commissioning father by AID. She carries the child and hands him/her over after birth. Through IVF it is also possible for the couple to contribute both sperm and eggs, so the surrogate mother is biologically unrelated to the child she bears.

Sometimes it is a sister, or even mother, who acts as the surrogate, or the contract may be arranged by an agency. In this country commercial surrogacy is illegal – which rules out the operation of surrogacy agencies.

What's wrong with surrogacy?

A couple desperate for their own child may be attracted to the idea of surrogacy as it provides a means of having a baby which will be at least partly genetically theirs. Against this, surrogacy deliberately splits child bearing from nurturing.

The child has two mothers. One carries the child in the womb for nine months, only to give him/her away with no further rights or responsibilities. The other claims to be the true mother but may not even be biologically related to the child.

The situation is most complicated where the child genetically belongs to the surrogate mother. Having given birth, the woman may be unwilling to hand over the baby.

The child's origins are confused and he/she may be unsure of where he/she truly belongs. The unrelated, nurturing mother may discover feelings of resentment or alienation from the child which is her husband's but not hers.

Difficulties could also arise if the child were born severely handicapped. None of the 'parents' involved may wish to take responsibility for the child.

© *Christian Action Research & Education*
(*CARE*)

A guide to IVF in Britain

How it works

1 IVF or in-vitro fertilisation means fertilisation outside the body.

2 The first successful 'test-tube' baby, Louise Brown, was born in 1978.

3 About 70 British clinics offer IVF.

4 Eggs and sperm are mixed outside the woman's body in a culture dish or test-tube.

5 Embryos are left to grow for about a day to check they are developing normally. Up to three embryos are transferred into the womb. If it is successful one or more embryos will implant in the womb lining.

6 Couples are referred to a consultant if they have been trying for a baby without success for two years.

7 NHS waiting lists are long. About 90 per cent of IVF treatments are done privately.

8 IVF costs from £700 to £2,500 per cycle. Most clinics suggest couples sign up for three cycles.

9 Latest figures, for 1993, show 18,000 women had 21,000 cycles of treatment, resulting in 3,089 live births.

How treatment varies

Criteria for access to NHS treatment varies widely. In the West Midlands region alone these are the rules:

1 Sandwell: You must be 34 or under, lived in the area three years. Max 3 cycles.

2 Dudley: You must be no more than 38 and the couple must be childless.

3 Hereford: No criteria at all.

4 Warwickshire: Do not fund treatment.

5 Wolverhampton: The woman must be no more than 38; the man no more than 50. No living children from either partner. Must have been in a stable heterosexual relationship for two years.

© *The Independent, April 1996*

What is embryo research and why is it needed?

Information from Progress Educational Trust

Embryo research is research using pre-embryos (or conceptuses) up to 14 days after fertilisation. Pre-embryo research investigates why problems such as genetic disorders, infertility and miscarriage occur in reproduction in order to prevent or treat them.

When a sperm fertilises an egg, the two nuclei join to produce one cell. This cell divides into two cells, which divide into four cells, and so on. They are, at this early stage, simply a cluster of undifferentiated cells. It is not until 14 days after fertilisation takes place that the cells begin to differentiate, and most of the cells begin to form placental tissue which then is only visible under a powerful microscope. After 14 days, separation is complete and the remaining cells, which did not separate into placental tissue, begin to form an embryo (sometimes two; this is the last stage at which identical twins may form). At this point of development the embryo is still no larger than this full stop. Only when implantation occurs is the woman said to be pregnant. If all goes well, the embryo grows into a foetus and eventually a baby. Sadly only about 20% of the embryos actually implant and produce a live birth.

Prevention of genetic disease

In the UK, genetic defects are a very common cause of disability and infant death. Genetic defects and congenital malformations occur in approximately 2-5% of all live births, causing 30% of childhood deaths. Research would be the key to detecting abnormalities in the first days after fertilisation. About 20% of pre-embryos are abnormal. However it is now possible to screen the pre-embryos of couples known to be at high risk of cystic fibrosis. Research is progressing in the diagnosis of other fatal childhood disorders such as Duchenne muscular dystrophy.

Over 50 types of severe congenital disease may one day be detectable by pre-embryo screening. Many patients, learning that their foetus is affected, will seek an abortion. The development of IVF may make it possible to be sure from the outset that a pregnancy carries no genetic abnormality.

Infertility treatment

Infertility affects at least one in ten couples. Without the pre-embryo research which has already been carried out, IVF could not have been developed. Continued research is essential to further improve IVF's success rate. Research is also working to help those with hormone problems or whose early embryos are not implanting properly.

Infertility is as common in men as it is in women. At the moment only 19% of infertile men are helped by surgery or hormone treatment.

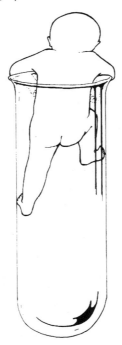

Donor insemination used to be the only alternative for many men. However, pre-embryo research has offered new hope to men with the introduction of techniques such as Sub Zonal Injection (SUZI) and Intra Cytoplasmic Injection (ICSI).

With these techniques a man may use his own sperm to fertilise his partners egg even if they are defective or immotile. Pre-embryo research also ensures that techniques used with IVF are safe and will not cause damage to a baby.

Diagnosis in fertility

Despite extensive tests, about 40,000 UK couples never discover why they are infertile. Some undergo up to ten years of repeated investigations and unsuccessful treatments, and suffer great distress. The study of sperm and eggs from such couples will improve diagnosis. It will then be possible to see if fertilisation takes place and embryos divide normally.

If there is no fertilisation, tests can be done to see which gamete is infertile by attempting fertilisation using gametes from fertile donors. This may pinpoint whether sperm or eggs are the root of the infertile couple's problem and could give clues for a solution. Such techniques could help in counselling couples about future prospects of pregnancy.

Research into miscarriage

Over one in five pregnancies (100,000) end in recognised miscarriage each year in the UK. Many more fertilised eggs do not survive long enough to become recognised miscarriages. Miscarriage may cause haemorrhage or infection; many women require hospital admission, anaesthesia, or even blood transfusion. Some women have the great emotional distress and shock of repeated miscarriage.

In over 85% of cases the cause of miscarriage is unknown; one of the main problems is chromosomal abnormality in the embryo. Research has just recently enabled doctors to detect these abnormalities in the pre-implantation embryo, resulting in a first successful pregnancy.

How will research help contraception?

Shortcomings in contraceptive methods are well documented and improvement is long overdue. New methods must be rigorously tested to minimise failure rates, side-effects and to ensure no adverse effect in case of pregnancy. Pre-embryo research could greatly help in these advances.

Could this research be done on animals?

Much preliminary research is done on animals, but before clinical use is made of a method it is essential to confirm it also works with human material. Animals have very different reproductive systems from humans; they do not suffer from the same genetic diseases and rarely suffer from repeated miscarriages.

Pre-embryo or pre-natal diagnosis?

Amniocentesis is a test for finding out whether a woman is carrying an abnormal foetus but it cannot be carried out until 14 to 16 weeks of pregnancy. A similar test called chorion villus sampling (CVS) tests for some abnormalities at around eight to ten weeks of pregnancy. If foetal abnormality is found by either test, the patient faces a difficult choice: to continue with the pregnancy or to consider having a termination. Amniocentesis and CVS both involve discomfort, a limited risk (about 1% with amniocentesis) of spontaneous abortion and a risk of damaging the foetus. However, the detection of abnormal genes or chromosomal defects in the pre-embryo would make it possible to transfer only normal pre-embryos to women whose families carry serious genetic diseases. This has now successfully occurred resulting in the first baby born following diagnosis of cystic fibrosis.

The scientific journal, *Nature*, argued in March 1985:

'The means of preventing the transmission of some severe and inherited diseases (with, incidentally, a concomitant reduction in the requirement of abortions in the "at risk" families) is therefore almost to hand, but their development and implementation will not be possible if research is not allowed.'

Controls on research

Before research starts researchers and doctors have to submit their full proposals to a local ethics committee. Approval is by no means automatic. Ethics committees have few or no members making research proposals. They have a strong lay presence; hospital committees take representatives from the outside community.

To meet any disquiet about research involving human pre-embryos, the Warnock Committee recommended that all research projects be approved by a statutory licensing body and be carried out under the supervision of a named licence holder, who would be strictly controlled. Unauthorised use of an in-vitro pre-embryo would then be a criminal offence.

Following this recommen-dation, and after extended debate in Parliament, the Human Fertilisation and Embryology Authority (HFEA) was appointed by the Government and became effective on 1 August 1991. Its constitutional duties are laid down in the Human Fertilisation and Embryology Act (1990). The authority approves and licenses all centres practising IVF and strictly monitors all pre-embryo research.

Public opinion

Opinion polls during the period of parliamentary discussion and activity consistently showed that many people are in favour of pre-embryo research particularly if the purpose is to prevent children being born with disability. In May 1985, MARPLAN found that 63% of those questioned were in favour of research on human pre-embryos up to 14 days in order to prevent congenital handicap.

In October 1989, NOP found that twice as many people approved as disapproved of research on human pre-embryos to improve and increase knowledge of disease and disability in newly born children.

In January 1990, Gallop found that 58% agreed with the use of the human embryo for research into genetic and chromosomal disorders.

© *Progress Education Trust*

In-vitro fertilisation treatments

National data for treatments carried out during the period April 1994 to the end of March 1995.

	Numbers	Live birth rates
Patients treated	19983	
Total number of cycles	25730	14.5%
Stimulated cycles	20855	14.9%
Unstimulated cycles[1]	594	1.3%
Frozen embryo transfers	3701	11.3%
Two embryo transfers	6799	15.8%
Micro manipulated cycles	1664	15.9%
Multiple birth rate[2]	28.7%	
Triplet birth rate[3]	3.7%	
Abandoned cycles	4718 (3.3%)	

[1] The number of unstimulated cycles **excludes** frozen embryo transfers and cycles using donated embryos.
[2] The multiple birth rate is the percentage of births where more than one baby was born.
[3] The triplet birth rate is the percentage of births where three babies were born.

Source: The patients' guide to DI and IVF clinics, Human Fertility and Embryology Authority

The ethics of embryo research

Information from Progress Educational Trust

There are compelling moral and ethical arguments in favour of embryo research. Many theologians, philosophers, medical ethicists and politicians offer their beliefs on embryo research in the following quotations extracted from briefings and speeches at the time of the 1989 parliamentary debate.

The relief of human suffering

We are talking about research which could be of great potential to humanity. Its prohibition could cause great sadness, pain and suffering and end the hopes of many hard-pressed and worried families not only for now but also in the future.

Lord Ennals, House of Lords, 7 December 1989

I am neither a doctor nor a scientist, but I believe that to refuse help to those who might be helped is contrary to both religion and humanity.

Baroness Warnock, House of Lords, December 1989

The pain and suffering of people with these disorders is real and the moral issue is whether society should prohibit research that could prevent the birth of future generations of affected individuals.

Genetic Interest Group statement

The principle reason for my view that embryo research should be allowed up to 14 days is that such research can make an important contribution to preventing the creation of grossly deformed and mentally handicapped babies. Such births are often very tragic for the child itself and for the parents concerned, most of whom bear the burden with immense devotion and courage.

Viscount Caldecote, House of Lords, 7 December 1989

As a committed Christian myself I believe that the performance of such research within the 14-day limit and under the strictest control of a statutory licensing body, with all the safeguards which the [Human Fertilisation and Embryology] Bill enshrines, is not only entirely compatible with the Christian ethic but will have untold benefit for human health.

Lord Walton of Detchant, December 1989

Where did I begin?

I believe that in the very early stage when personal attributes are non-existent and when identity is yet to be established there is room to allow experiment. But it has to be hedged round by safeguards which make it publicly obvious that respect for our human origins is being properly observed.

Archbishop of York, House of Lords, 15 January 1988

If we are talking . . . about the origin of an individual life, one can trace back directly from the newborn baby to the foetus, and back further to the origin of the individual embryo at the primitive streak stage in the embryonic plate at sixteen or seventeen days. If one tries to trace back further than that there is no longer a coherent entity. Instead there is a larger collection of cells, some of which are going to take part in the subsequent development of the embryo and some of which aren't.

Dr Anne MacLaren, FRS, 'Human Embryo Research: Yes or No?' 1986

. . . but if you were to try to go forward in time, i.e. start with given gametes and move forward to an individual, you wouldn't be able to do the same thing, because in most cases there would be no final individual, in any sense that we understand.

Dr Bernadette Modell, Human Embryo Research

Is research unnatural?

. . . scientific intervention at this point is precisely to increase selectivity in an evolutionary process in which what to us is waste is in fact a selection for biological evolutionary ends.

The Reverend Professor Gordon Dunstan, 'Human Embryo Research: Yes or No?' 1986

Good medical practice

When the choice is required between the welfare of the mother-to-be who 'is' and a pre-embryo which as yet 'is not', the overarching law of compassion for the living must be the moral priority . . . I believe that the welfare of the potential mother must take precedence over the welfare of a pre-embryo. The embryo can be expendable, the mother – never.

The Reverend Lord Soper, statement to PROGRESS

I believe that research must continue if in-vitro fertilisation is to continue. One cannot separate them, and I regard as totally unrealistic and indeed immoral any proposal to continue in-vitro fertilisation without a proper backing in research.

Archbishop of York, House of Lords, 15 January 1988

Such a revolutionary approach as the pre-implantation diagnosis of genetic disease would reduce both the need and the number of pregnancy terminations. This goal can never be achieved unless the technique is perfected and proved to be safe, and this cannot be established without research using the human pre-embryo.

Dr Virginia Bolton et al, 'Freedom to Choose', published by PROGRESS

As a Christian, I believe that God gave us the ability to put our brains to good use so that progress can be made; but he also gave us the wisdom to build in the necessary safeguards to prevent our misuse of that ability.

Lord Glenarthur, House of Lords, 7 December 1989

Those who stress the continuities (scientists and biologists) and those who stress the discontinuities (the general public) may be totally united in their belief that human life is sacred and is not to be destroyed except in the face of overwhelming necessity. The differences between them lie in their perception of when and how human life begins, and this is not a matter on which our Christian sources give us any clear guidance.

Archbishop of York, 'Beginnings: The Archbishop's Letter', 1989

... to acknowledge that we are being destined to learn from experience immediately forces us to consider the crucial question of the relationship between what we are accustomed to call 'nature' (e.g. the 'natural processes' of our human nature in its physical/biological dimension) and ethics. Many moral theologians, myself included, would tackle this question along the following lines:
1. Evolution is a natural process. As human beings we have come into being through the process of evolution and live as a part of a cosmos which is in a continuing process of evolution;
2. Human intelligence has come about through the process of evolution and so is 'natural'. Consequently it can be argued that:
a   It is now 'natural' for human intelligence to play its part in directing the evolutionary process;
b. The fact that something is 'artificial' (an artefact or technology produced by human intelligence) does not of itself make it 'unnatural'.
3. The evolutionary process works through trial and error; moral significance should not be read into processes simply because they are 'natural'. Both nature and intelligence can make mistakes.

Father Kevin T Kelly, 'The Month', March 1990
© Progress Educational Trust

The fertility right man can no longer count on

Men in the West are producing only half the sperm they were a decade ago, says a study.

The discovery will renew speculation that a build-up of man-made chemicals in the environment could be to blame.

The latest study – by a team from Helsinki University – reinforces earlier findings on sperm counts and poor semen quality.

Unless the trend is halted, boys born 60 years from now could be infertile.

The Finnish research team, whose findings are reported in the *British Medical Journal*, also noted that the weight of men's testicles fell significantly from an average 18.9 grams in 1981 to 17.8 grams in 1991.

During the ten years of the survey, say the researchers, the proportion of men who had the normal biological processes leading to sperm production fell from 56.4 per cent to 26.9 per cent.

By Jenny Hope, Medical Correspondent

Over the same period there was a significant increase in the number of cases in which no mature sperm cells were found. The figure rose from eight per cent to 20 per cent.

Scientists made the discovery after post-mortem examinations on 528 mostly middle-aged men from Finland who died between 1981 to 1991. The results contribute to mounting evidence on diminishing male fertility originally highlighted in Scandinavian research in 1992 and reinforced by an analysis of 61 separate studies involving 15,000 men in Western countries.

A British study in February from Dr Stewart Irvine, of the Medical Research Council's reproductive biology unit in Edinburgh, added to the disquiet.

It showed that men born in the 1970s produced on average 25 per cent fewer sperm than those born in the 1950s.

Some experts have suggested that the build-up of man-made chemicals in the environment, many of which can mimic female hormones, could be interfering with male development.

But Dr Jarkko Pajarinen's Helsinki team concluded that the changes they found could not be explained by any known risk factors.

They were not explained by drugs, smoking or alcohol and more research was clearly needed to find the reason, they said.

Dr Charles Tyler, senior lecturer in reproductive biology at Brunel University, agreed.

He said yesterday: 'We need to target research at groups of men who have been exposed to high levels of certain chemicals, weigh up the evidence and decide on remedial action.'

© The Daily Mail January, 1997

Doctor offers parents a choice of baby's sex

By David Fletcher, Health Correspondent

A test-tube baby doctor is to launch the world's first fertility service to create babies of whichever sex their parents require in return for fees of £8,000-£10,000.

Dr Paul Rainsbury, medical director of a private hospital in Redbridge, Essex, is setting up the 'designer baby' service at a hospital in Riyadh, Saudi Arabia.

Treatment will initially be carried out in Naples, Italy, where regulations are less strict than in Britain – which bans sex selection of babies for social reasons.

His plans were condemned as unethical by leading test-tube baby specialists and by the National Fertility Association. The Human Fertilisation and Embryology Authority said he would not be allowed to provide the service in Britain.

Mr Rainsbury, medical director at Roding Hospital, Redbridge, rejected suggestions that he was 'playing God'.

He said: 'Those who work in the field of human reproduction are accustomed to censure, usually by people who have no idea of the huge distress caused by infertility and childlessness.

'My hope is that any criticism will disappear as people come to understand why we have decided to use existing medical science to help those who face intense personal pressure to produce babies of a specific sex.'

He expected to see similar projects emerging after he had borne the brunt of initial criticism.

'Offering sex selection as part of infertility treatment was always going to come. It was simply a question of who would be first to grasp the nettle.

'I hope that well within a further 20 years' time, choosing the sex of a baby will be accepted around the

How it works

A cell is removed from a test-tube embryo and its chromosomes are examined to see if it is male or female.

An embryo of the right sex will be implanted. Otherwise it will be destroyed.

The technique, costing at least £4,000, is more reliable than a previous method – separating sperm according to sex chromosomes.

world, and I see this as the start of that process.'

He said couples taking part would be required to have counselling before being accepted and would be told that normal pregnancy rates for assisted conception would apply – about one in three for a first attempt by young healthy couples.

He said two British couples had already requested treatment but the service was mostly expected to attract couples from the Middle and Far East where cultural, religious and economic factors traditionally place great importance on continuing the male family line.

Sex selection was pioneered by Lord Winston, head of the fertility clinic at Hammersmith Hospital, west London, and is allowed in Britain only for couples carrying a genetic disease which would be passed on to their children.

Lord Winston said sex selection was still an experimental procedure which could result in damage to the embryo and should not be used except where there was no alternative.

He said: 'I find it incredible that he can set up a clinic to do this work in Saudi Arabia when very few people have managed to achieve it in very sophisticated laboratories.

'It is a technique which should be used only to overcome the inheritance of sex-linked diseases and not for social reasons.'

Peter Brinsden, medical director of Bourn Hall, a leading test-tube baby clinic, said: 'It is not ethically acceptable to use this technique.

'I get letters every month from couples asking if we can help them to have a male baby. I have to say, "Sorry, but this is not acceptable legally or ethically".'

Tim Hedgley, director of the National Fertility Association, also condemned the practice as unethical.

© Telegraph Group Limited, London 1997

IVF and embryo research

A humanist view

Humanists respect life, but are not religious and do not believe in the 'sanctity of life'. There is no evidence for a creator god and humans are a natural product of evolution. The most important consideration in questions of life and death is the quality of life for each individual.

Humans have long intervened in reproductive processes:

- We have controlled the breeding of certain animals, both domestic (such as hunting dogs in earlier centuries, and pet dogs and cats now) and livestock (such as cattle and sheep). Without human intervention, most modern farm animals and pets would not exist in the form we see today.
- We have introduced contraception.
- Most recently we have helped people have children, using techniques such as fertility drugs, in-vitro fertilisation (IVF, commonly thought alongside the phrase 'test-tube babies'), sperm donation, and surrogate motherhood.

Britain has a carefully written law governing many aspects of intervention in human reproduction, and associated research which involves early stage embryos. It is called the Human Fertilisation and Embryology Act.

Some ethical implications of IVF

Firstly it is important to remember that the specific situation may be very influential on ethical thinking. It is difficult to devise an ethical rule that can apply to all situations related to complicated subjects like this.

The first consideration must be the predicted quality of life of any children produced in this way. Secondly, consent is important:

Robert Ashby, Director, British Humanist Association

especially the mother's genuine and informed consent to this technique. Thirdly, if the man who provides the sperm for the fertilisation is not the partner of the mother, his views on his future involvement with the child have to be listened to, and an agreement drawn up before any treatment is started.

IVF and other fertility treatments are usually quite expensive. If the National Health is paying for the treatment, it is sensible that alternatives (such as adoption) are considered first. The question of whether a woman has an absolute human right to have her own children is a difficult one. However, most humanists would place greatest importance on the mother's views.

Some ethical implications of embryo research

Early stage embryos (or 'pre-embryos') are a collection of cells arising from division of a fertilised

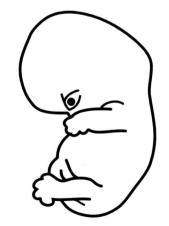

Britain has a carefully written law governing many aspects of intervention in human reproduction

---

human egg. At this stage the cells have not begun to form into specialist cells that would form particular parts of a human body. They have no consciousness and no means of feeling pain. Although such a pre-embryo has the potential to develop into a human, it isn't the same as a human when it is at this early stage.

A humanist would consider what suffering might be involved. Clearly there is no evidence for a pre-embryo feeling pain or emotions. The source of the pre-embryo would also be important. If it would exist anyway, whether wanted by researchers or not, the source would not be important. However, if it was produced specially for the research, by IVF in the laboratory, most humanists would want to be sure there was very careful regulation of that production, and the aims and methods of the experiments to be carried out.

Humanists would also need to look at specific examples. If, say, research on pre-embryos might lead to discovery of new treatments to prevent or cure diseases that cause suffering to many humans, the experiment may have great value to the quality of human life. If the research aims did not have such potential, then a humanist might well be against the experiment.

Research on more developed embryos or foetuses is far more complicated. Doctors and other scientists are not absolutely agreed on when a foetus is developed enough to feel pain, or when it develops human consciousness. On these questions, different humanists are likely to have different opinions – just as many religious people will differ from their fellow believers.

© *British Humanist Association*
January, 1997

Fertility / infertility

Information from ISSUE (The National Fertility Association)

Most people grow up believing that they will be able to plan their families. That is, they will be able to decide whether to have children, how many to have and when to have them. Yet for a surprisingly large number of people this simply isn't true. Many find that pregnancy does not occur when they wish it to.

As a species human beings are not very fertile. A couple has, on average, only a 20-25% chance of conceiving each month. This figure may surprise those who are able to have children easily. It will not surprise the 1 in 6 couples who find they need medical help to have a child.

When is the best time to try for a pregnancy?

During the first part of a woman's monthly cycle, her ovaries prepare to release an egg. The release of an egg, known as ovulation, occurs between day 10 and day 18 of a 29-day cycle. The process of ovulation is controlled by hormones. A rapid rise in levels of luteinising hormone (LH) occurs 24-36 hours before ovulation. This may be measured by ovulation detection kits, such as Clearplan One Step, which are available from most chemists.

Ovulation may also be detected by using natural family planning methods which involve monitoring changes in body temperature in combination with changes in cervical mucus and changes in the position of the cervix itself. Monitoring changes in body temperature alone is not sufficient. For further information on natural family planning methods and how they may be used to monitor your fertility please seek the advice of your local family planning clinic.

For a pregnancy to occur, the couple should be having sex frequently, in the week before ovulation. This is when the women is at her most fertile. During sexual intercourse, sperm are deposited in the woman's vagina at ejaculation. They travel up though the womb into the woman's fallopian tube , if they meet an egg, fertilisation may occur. For a pregnancy to become established the fertilised egg must then travel down to the womb and attach itself to one of the walls.

Difficulties can arise at any stage in the process.

- sexual intercourse may not be happening regularly around the time of ovulation;
- there may be problems with the egg or sperm;
- any blockages in either the man or the woman's reproductive tract can prevent a pregnancy from occurring.

Problems can arise equally in men and women. For some people the cause of such infertility cannot be found. This is known as 'unexplained infertility'. In a number of cases, there may be more than one cause. Some couples have a child, but then experience difficulty in having second or subsequent children, Thus situation is known as 'secondary infertility'.

Treatment for infertility

There are several different treatments for infertility. They range from drug treatment either by mouth of by injection to the more technical forms such as in-vitro fertilisation (IVF). Donor treatment – using donated sperm, eggs or fertilised eggs (embryos) – is an option for some couples.

Before treatment is offered, medical investigations should be carried out to ascertain the cause or causes of the sub-fertility.

Counselling is of immense value. For some treatments, such as donor treatment, it is a requirement that counselling is provided. It is advisable that offers of counselling are accepted.

When should help be sought for infertility?

Infertility is defined as the lack of a pregnancy following 12 months of regular sex without the use of contraception. Help should be sought if:

- the couple meet the infertility criteria described above
- the woman had absent or missed periods
- she has had abdominal or pelvic surgery
- she is 33 or over
- the man has had surgery in the region of his groin or injury to the testicles
- either partner has had a sexually transmitted disease
- there is a possible genetic reason

The first step in seeking help is to consult your GP. He or she will have access to your medical records and will be able to start the necessary investigations. She or he may refer you on to your local hospital or clinic.

© ISSUE (*The National Fertility Association*)

Briefing on human embryo research

Information from LIFE

Some facts about the technique of IVF

Fertility drugs are used to induce superovulation, and because of the risk of multiple pregnancies, only three will be replaced, resulting in the so-called 'spare' embryos. Sadly many people who are against the creation of embryos specifically for research, fell for the argument that these 'spare' embryos would ultimately die anyway, and so what was the harm in using them for research? They totally overlooked the fact that 'spare' embryos would never exist if it were not for the use of the fertility drugs.

So why are they using these fertility drugs? Louise Brown (the first test-tube baby) was attempt number 104. In those days they were not using any drugs and were collecting one egg at a time from natural monthly cycles. They thought that if they could put more than one embryo back then the changes of getting pregnant would be increased.

However, many things have improved since then – for instance they discovered that the tiny irregularities in the lining of the tubing used to collect the eggs, particularly at joins between two bits of tubing, was damaging the eggs. Now the entire inside length of the whole tubing system is teflon-coated. All centres have now reduced the numbers of embryos that are transferred back (the ILA now recommends no more than three). It has now been recognised that the superovulation treatment itself introduces problems of its own. The sky-high hormone levels produced make the lining of the womb less receptive to the implantation of an embryo, in addition the eggs are of a 'lower' quality and often many do not fertilise. I have come across

publications where they are now returning to collecting single eggs from women who are given no fertility drugs (i.e. a normal unstimulated monthly cycle). They have achieved a 17% success rate (*Fertility and Sterility*, October 1989 page 617). It's very interesting that those who are doing research say that the success of this technique in their hands is only 3%! I wonder why this discrepancy?

Claim: Embryo research is needed to treat and eliminate congenital and inherited diseases.

The second arm of the pro-research campaign was that embryo research would help eliminate genetic diseases. Some MPs got letters from couples who had children with these diseases, and genuinely believed that their children could be cured if only embryo research was allowed to continue. Eventually in response to the Parliamentary Medical and Scientific Pro-Life Advisory Committee, Progress, our opponents pushing for embryo research, had to admit that 'Research using human pre-embryos is not, and never has been, concerned with the treatment of genetic disorders or chromosomal abnormalities.'

The Royal College of Physicians produced a report in September 1989 which states: 'Most infants with congenital malformations and chromosomal disorders were born to healthy young women with no previously identifiable risk factors. It

seems unlikely that these sporadic disorders can be prevented.' Another fact that people don't realise is that a congenital abnormality is not necessarily the same as an inherited disease. For instance spina bifida – certainly a congenital abnormality – is not due to any simple genetic abnormality. In fact only 15-20% of congenital problems are due to simple genetic abnormalities.

Professor Winston, to support his embryo biopsy technique, used the following argument – and I quote him directly 'These parents would avoid the dilemma posed by prenatal diagnosis later in gestation – whether or not to abort a much wanted but affected foetus' (*Lancet*, 18 February 1989 page 347.) Those who are against abortion, if they are logical in their thinking, must, for identical reasons, also be opposed to embryo biopsy and destruction. The arguments that embryo 'testing' is less traumatic to patients psychologically than amniocentesis and subsequent abortion totally ignores the stress associated with IVF. (*Human Reproduction*, December 1989 supplement page 17.)

What sort of embryo research is being done?

If embryo research was essential to improving IVF then all research would be to that aim. One only has to examine the list of projects licensed by the ILA to see that improving the success rate of IVF is not the motive for much of the research. Many are of a pure science nature, others are more sinister. I will give you just four examples of the type of work being done, admittedly not all from this country.

1. Many of you will remember the thalidomide tragedy. This was a drug which helped relieve morning sickness. The story of how the drug

company ignored the growing evidence that it was producing babies with no arms or legs is an eye-opener in itself. Anyway now, many years later, scientists are still intrigued into how and why thalidomide caused these deformities. In one medical journal I came across the following horrendous study using thalidomide. It was published in 1989. You may recall how even the pro-research doctors were saying that there was no need to do research after 14 days. Well in this study they were using 4-week-old embryos. And where did they get the embryos from? I will quote verbatim from the journal: 'from healthy mothers through the collaborating obstetricians'. I.e. from very carefully carried out early abortions. These abortions must have been very carefully carried out because many of the embryos were intact and still inside the amniotic sac (i.e. the fluid sac in which the baby grows.) They then carefully dissected the developing arms off from the embryos, and transferred them to special 'organ culture' plates. Half were left to grow normally, and thalidomide was given to the other half. After a period of growth they were then examined under the microscope. (*Analytical Cellular Pathology*, 1989 volume 1, page 247.)

2. Would you believe that embryologists were not sure if an early IVF embryo looked the same as one conceived naturally? They therefore asked a woman who was requesting sterilisation to become deliberately pregnant. By taking 8-hourly blood tests and measuring the hormone levels they could calculate the exact time of ovulation. When ovulation occurred she was told to go to bed with her partner and six days later she had her sterilisation, and her developing baby was recovered and then examined under the microscope. (*Human Reproduction*, 1989 volume 4 page 680.)

3. All through the campaign you heard about infertile couples, and how embryo research would help them. The scientists are also interested in the embryo for testing contraceptives, abortion vaccines and the abortion drug RU486. As long ago as 1969 this was being discussed. In September of 1969 there was a conference held in London which had the title 'International Population Union Conference on the Scientific Study of Population'. During that conference it was stated that a supply of human embryos for research was considered an essential ingredient in developing techniques to combat pregnancy. Two quotations from the conference proceedings are as follows: 'Work is required to seek compounds that would appear in the tubal fluid at an adequate concentration to be toxic to the zygote (i.e. early embryo) without manifesting general toxicity,' and when discussing contraceptive vaccines they said

'work on the process of in-vitro fertilisation, is therefore directly cogent to this problem'. More recently in the 14th annual report of the WHO Special Programme's Task Force on Vaccines for Fertility Regulation, published in 1985, the following statement is made: 'The embryo represents an ideal target for attack since it comes into contact with the maternal circulation at a very early stage in its development.'

4. And finally we come to RU486, the new abortion drug. In 1988 the *British Journal of Obstetrics and Gynaecology* published a study (June 1988 page 592) carried out in Aberdeen, on the effect of RU486 on the in-vitro fertilisation and development of human embryos. In this study, 48 women requesting sterilisation were superovulated, 24 of them were given RU486 thirty-five hours before egg collection, with the other half acting as 'controls'. All the eggs collected were then fertilised, grown, and examined. The conclusion was that RU486 had no effect on the final growth of the egg, fertilisation or subsequent growth of the embryo and so – 'diminished the possibility of its use as a once-a-month contraceptive drug'.

So now you can clearly see that far from being used to help the infertile, embryos are being used to test the efficiency of their own destruction.

© LIFE

10 ways to make a baby without making love

AID

(Artificial insemination by donor)
Used where there is no sperm in the semen sample or if the male suffers from a hereditary disease. Sperm from an anonymous donor is used to inseminate the female artificially. This widely accepted and legal method results in thousands of births every year. It's important that couples using this method have a stable relationship and can cope with

Complied by Paula Hunter

potential emotional and ethical problems.
- Average cost: Around £800
- Success rate: 11%

AIH

(Artificial insemination by husband)
The male produces a semen sample directly into a sterile container. The sperm is then drawn up into a syringe attached to a short plastic tube and 'injected' around the cervix and within the cervical canal. Sometimes recommended for men with a low sperm count or poor sperm motility, in the hope that introducing the sperm directly into the cervical canal will protect them from the acidity of the vagina and help to shorten their journey to the

egg. Available on the NHS, but waiting lists can be as long as four years.

- Average cost: Around £800
- Success rate: 11%

IVF
(In-vitro fertilisation)
This usually follows a month-long drugs course involving nasal inhalants and injections to super-activate the ovaries and promote egg production. The eggs are allowed to mature before being extracted by a fine needle through the vagina. Eggs and sperm are then combined in a dish to fertilise; a maximum of three may be inserted into the woman's uterus. Treatment is available on the NHS, but couples can face a two-year wait and are taken off the list when the woman is 35.

- Average cost per treatment: £2,200
- Success rate: 14.2%

ZIFT
(Zygote intra-Fallopian transfer)
Eggs are fertilised in a laboratory through IVF and any that develop into embryos are transferred into the Fallopian tubes under general anaesthetic.

They're then left to travel naturally into the uterus. Difficult to obtain on the NHS.

- Average cost: Around £2,000
- Success rate: 3.5%

SUZI/MIST
(Sub-zonal insemination or Micro-insemination sperm transfer)
Used where there's a low sperm count. Eggs are collected as in IVF then five to ten sperm are injected beneath the layer of cells surrounding the egg (zona) or an opening is made in the zona to allow easier access of sperm to the egg. The eggs are then placed in the uterus. Not generally available on the NHS.

- Average cost: As high as £3,000
- Success rate: 2.5%

Egg donation
Eggs are anonymously donated to couples where the female partner is in her late 30s or older, has gone through an early menopause, or doesn't ovulate. The eggs are then fertilised in a test-tube with her partner's sperm and placed in her womb. Available on the NHS. Waiting time is shorter for private patients.

- Average cost: £850-£4,500
- Success rate: 6.5%

GIFT
(Gamete intra-Fallopian transfer)
Under general anaesthetic, a laparoscope (a long, thin hollow tube) is used to insert a single egg and sperm directly into the Fallopian tube via an incision in the abdomen. Any embryos that then develop travel down the tube and into the uterus. Not generally available on the NHS.

- Average cost: £2,000
- Success rate: 2.2%

IUI
(Intra-uterine insemination)
A relatively cheap and common technique in which a catheter is used to introduce the most motile sperm directly into the woman's uterus. It's particularly effective where the male has a low sperm count, poor sperm movement or where sperm have a problem interacting with cervical mucus (i.e. they're killed off in the cervix). Not generally available on the NHS.

- Average cost: From £325 during a natural cycle (when an egg has just been released) or £360 for a stimulated cycle (where the woman is given a drug to speed up ovulation).
- Success rate: 12-20%

ICSI
(Intra-cytoplasmic sperm injection)
A recently developed technique in which a single sperm is introduced directly into an egg. Up to three fertilised eggs are then placed in the uterus. A suitable method where sperm count is low, or motility so poor that the sperm cannot penetrate the egg. Not generally available on the NHS.

- Average cost: £2,950 if done privately
- Success rate: 4.2%

Surrogacy
Probably the most controversial method of conception. Sperm from the male is artificially implanted into a surrogate mother, using an egg donated by the surrogate or one from the female partner. The baby is handed over to the couple with the surrogate mother giving up all parental rights. In the US legislation makes this a straightforward transaction, but it's a grey area in the UK. It is currently illegal to pay a surrogate mother anything but expenses. If she decides to keep the baby, there is little a couple can do.

- Average cost: Anything up to £10,000
- Success rate: 15%

© SHE, July, 1996

INDEX